REVISED AND EXPANDED
GIANT BASIC SKILLS™
2nd GRADE WORKBOOK

Modern Publishing
A Division of Unisystems, Inc.
New York, New York 10022
Series UPC #49115

Cover art by Francesca Rizzo
Illustrated by Arthur Friedman
Educational Consultant, Shirley Consodine Granahan, M.S.

TO THE PARENTS

Dear Parents,

You're obviously interested in your child's education. After all, you purchased this book to help your child master the basic skills needed in daily life, from reading information to problem solving. As you and your child spend time together learning, you help to build the child's self-esteem, which is as important for success as the curriculum concepts in this book.

We suggest that when you use the book with your child, you try to follow these guidelines:

- Choose a time when both you and your child are relaxed.

- Don't try too many pages in a single sitting.

- Make sure your child has pencils, crayons, markers, or other writing tools.

- Encourage your child to browse through the book to find subject matter that catches his or her attention.

- Assure your child that it's okay to ask you questions as he or she works.

- Allow your child to work as independently as he or she feels confident to.

- Follow up by helping your child relate the stories, writing activities, and math problems to everyday experiences.

- Enjoy your time together, and always praise your child's effort.

- Encourage your child to use the practice pages provided at the end of the MATH, GRAMMAR, WRITING, and THINKING SKILLS sections to work independently and reinforce skills.

- Use the Achievement Checklist to keep track of which pages you need to revisit. When the "Mastered" column is full, your child has earned the diploma at the back of the book!

Happy learning!

ESSENTIAL SKILLS

Repetition is an effective way of forming a habit. The repeated use of important skills in these activities will help those skills become second nature to your child. When basic reading, math, grammar, phonics, writing, and thinking skills become a habit, success becomes a habit as well.

CHAPTER 1 ABC Order
Letter knowledge is an essential tool for decoding words. In this chapter, children hone their ability to **recognize initial letters** by their sounds. They then apply this skill to exercises in **alphabetizing words**.

CHAPTER 2 Phonics
This section focuses on the relationship between sounds and their symbols. Activities cover **long and short vowel sounds**, **digraphs**, **diphthongs**, **consonants**, and **consonant blends**.

CHAPTER 3 Reading Skills
Activities test children's ability to recognize words and read passages for meaning. Children investigate **classification**, **cause and effect**, **predicting outcomes**, **synonyms**, **antonyms**, **homonyms**, and **reading comprehension**, including **finding the main idea and supporting details**, **comparing and contrasting**, **making inferences**, and reconstructing the **sequence of events**.

CHAPTER 4 Math
Children explore many aspects of math and practice their skills with **addition**, **subtraction**, **place value and regrouping**, **multiplication**, **counting by 5s and 10s**, **measurement**, **money**, **geometric figures**, **fractions**, and **interpreting graphs**. Children also discover the differences between **odd and even** and **cardinal and ordinal numbers**, and learn place value to hundreds.

CHAPTER 5 Grammar
What is a **sentence**? What are nouns verbs, adjectives, and adverbs? These and other questions are answered in activities that explore **compound words**, **parts of speech**, **sentence parts**, **punctuation and capitalization**, **contractions**, **possessives**, **and spelling rules**.

DICTIONARY
This special section introduces second graders to how to use a dictionary. Important vocabulary is presented through simple definitions and example sentences. The part of speech is included with each definition to reinforce understanding of grammar concepts.

CHAPTER 6 Writing
Children practice various forms of writing, beginning with **sentences** and moving on to **paragraphs**. **Friendly letters**, **descriptive writing**, and **poetry** are explored in exercises that challenge children's creativity.

CHAPTER 7 Thinking Skills
Doing the kinds of **puzzles** and activities they like best, children use their skills in **visual discrimination**, **matching**, **sorting**, **patterning**, **finding and creating analogies**, **following map directions**, and **deduction**. Like detectives, children learn that everything in life provides clues we can follow to help us understand the things around us.

TABLE OF CONTENTS

ABC Order 6

Phonics 13

Reading Skills 39

Math 67

Grammar 138

DICTIONARY 195

Writing 227

Thinking Skills 238

Answers 279

Achievement Checklist 317

Diploma 320

ABC ORDER

The encyclopedia lists words in ABC order.
Look at each picture at the bottom of the page.
Draw a line to the book in which you would find it.
The first one has been done for you.

Skills: Understanding how to sequence in ABC order

ABC ORDER

The encyclopedia lists words in ABC order.
Draw a line from each picture to the book in which you would find it.

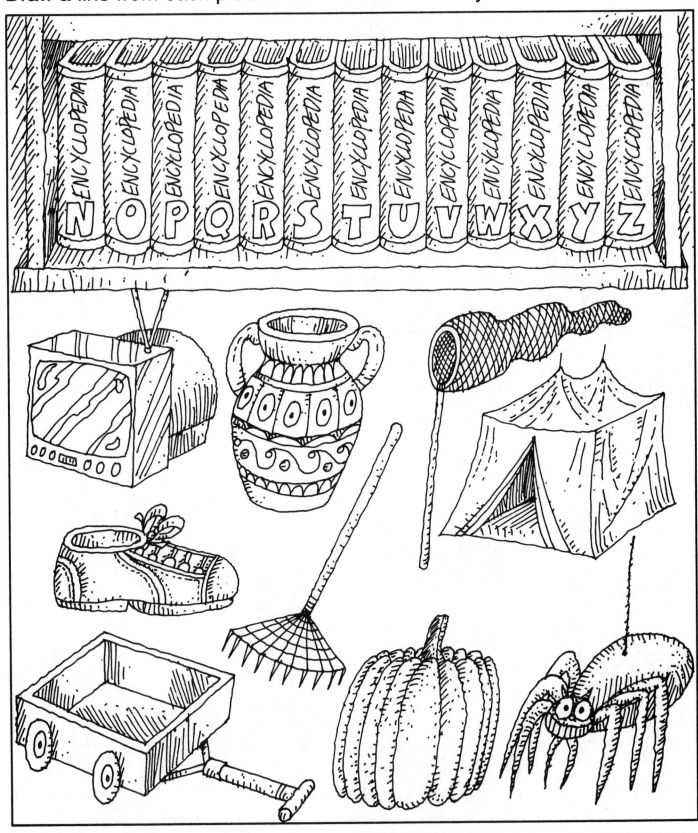

Skills: Understanding how to sequence in ABC order

ABC ORDER

Something is hiding. What can it be?
Follow the dots in ABC order and you will see!

Skills: Following ABC order

ABC ORDER

Look at the pictures and words.
Write the words in ABC order.
The first one has been done for you.

a b c d e f g h i j k l m n o p q r s t u v w x y z

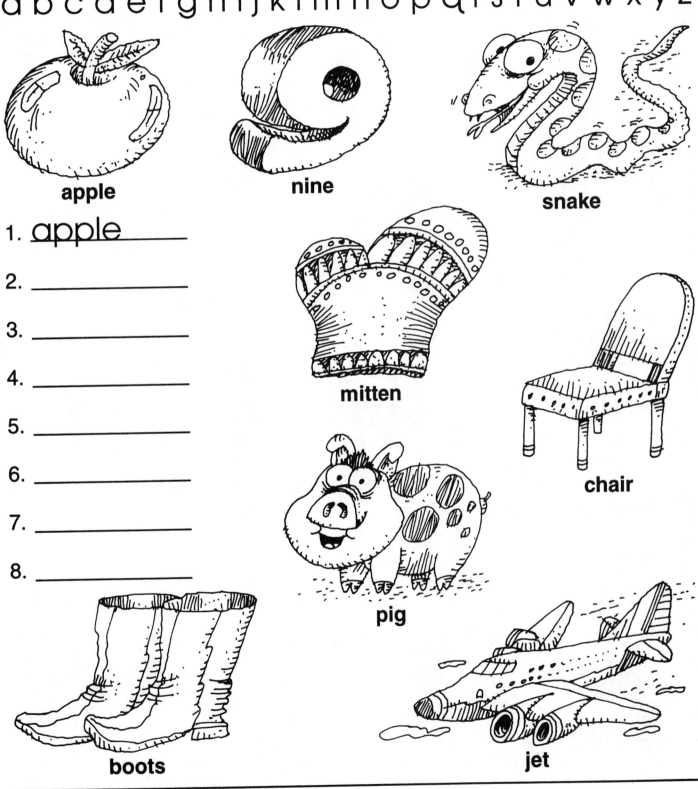

apple

nine

snake

1. <u>apple</u>

2. _____

3. _____

4. _____

5. _____

6. _____

7. _____

8. _____

mitten

chair

pig

boots

jet

Skills: Organizing and writing words in ABC order

ABC ORDER

Look at the pictures and words.
Write the words in ABC order.

hand

doll

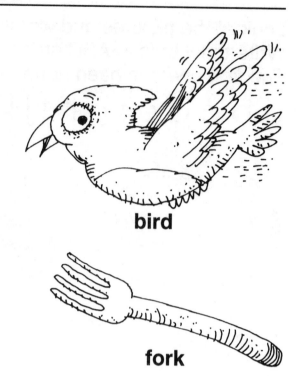

bird

fork

1. _____

2. _____

3. _____

4. _____

5. _____

6. _____

7. _____

8. _____

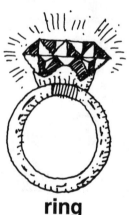

ring

cake

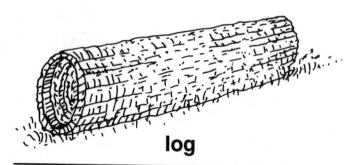

log

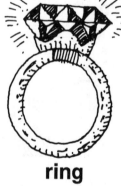

sun

Skills: Organizing and writing words in ABC order

ABC ORDER

You want to put words in ABC order. But three words start with the same letter!
What should you do? Look at the second letter in each word.
Put the second letters in ABC order.
Write the words in each row in ABC order.

a b c d e f g h i j k l m n o p q r s t u v w x y z

bus **bat** **bring**	1. _____	2. _____	3. _____
ship **sand** **silly**	1. _____	2. _____	3. _____
will **water** **wolf**	1. _____	2. _____	3. _____
fall **funny** **fox**	1. _____	2. _____	3. _____
ride **read** **roll**	1. _____	2. _____	3. _____

Skills: Alphabetizing words that start with the same letter

ABC ORDER

The wall is covered with letters.
But two letters are missing. Write them here: ____ ____

Skills: Recognizing letters; Visualizing missing letters

PHONICS

Vowels are the letters **a**, **e**, **i**, **o**, and **u**.
Each vowel has a short sound and a long sound.
You hear the **short** sound of:

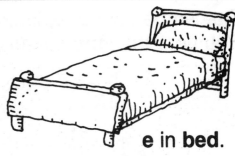

e in **bed**.

o in **box**.

a in **cat**.

i in **pin**.

u in **sun**.

Look at each picture below. Say its name.
Listen for the **short** vowel sound.
Circle the vowel you hear.
The first has been done for you.

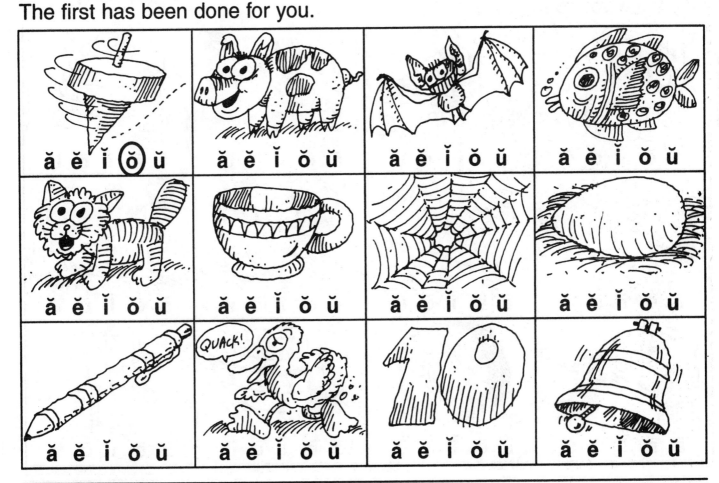

Skills: Recognition of short vowel sounds

PHONICS

Remember that **a**, **e**, **i**, **o**, and **u** have short and long sounds.
You hear the **long** sound of:

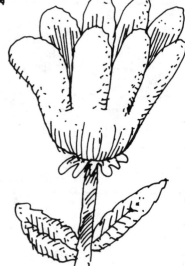

a in **cake**.

e in **bee**.

i in **bike**.

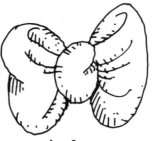

o in **bow**.

u in **tulip**.

Say each picture name.
Listen for the **long** vowel sound.
Circle the vowel you hear.

ā ē ī ō ū	ā ē ī ō ū	ā ē ī ō ū	ā ē ī ō ū
ā ē ī ō ū	ā ē ī ō ū	ā ē ī ō ū	ā ē ī ō ū
ā ē ī ō ū	ā ē ī ō ū	ā ē ī ō ū	ā ē ī ō ū

Skills: Recognition of long vowel sounds

PHONICS

Name each picture.
Circle the vowel sound you hear.
Write **S** if it is a short vowel sound. Write **L** if it is a long vowel sound.
The first one has been done for you.

ⓐ e i o u **S**

a e i o u ____

a e i o u ____

a e i o u ____

a e i o u ____

a e i o u ____

a e i o u ____

a e i o u ____

a e i o u ____

a e i o u ____

a e i o u ____

a e i o u ____

Skills: Recognition of short and long vowel sounds

PHONICS

Name each picture.
Write **a**, **e**, **i**, **o**, or **u** to tell which vowel sound you hear.
Then circle **S** if it is a short vowel sound. Circle **L** if it is a long sound.
The first one has been done for you.

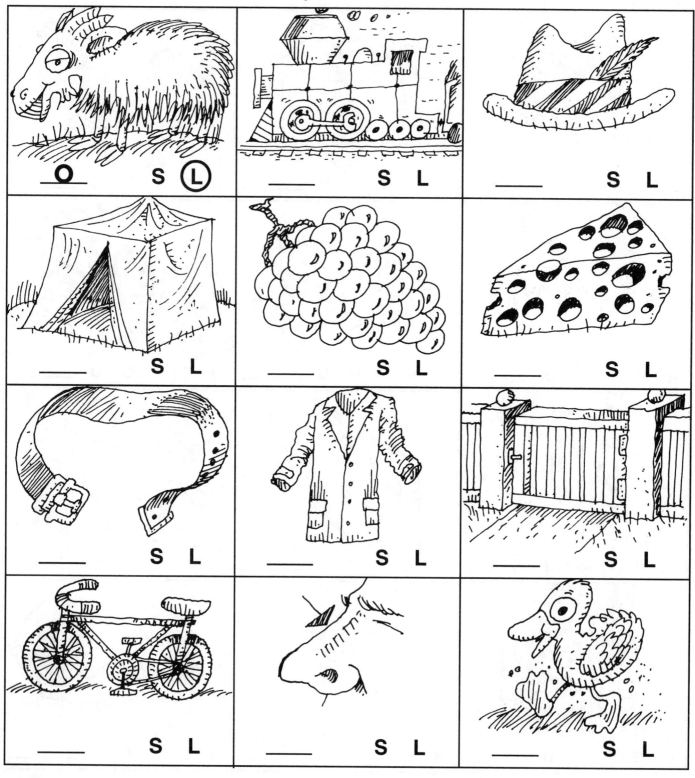

O S Ⓛ	___ S L	___ S L
___ S L	___ S L	___ S L
___ S L	___ S L	___ S L
___ S L	___ S L	___ S L

Skills: Recognition of short and long vowel sounds

PHONICS

When a word has two vowels, the first one usually takes its long sound.
The second vowel is silent, as in **rain**, **neat**, **pie**, **boat**, **suit** and **late**.
Some people remember this rule by saying,
"When two vowels go walking, the first one does the talking!"

Read each sentence.
Circle each word that has a **long vowel** sound.

I like to rake leaves.

We like to skate.

My bike has two wheels.

It is really neat to play the flute!

Skills: Recognizing double-vowel long vowel sounds

PHONICS

Complete each sentence.
Write the word that has a **long vowel** sound.

Is that a _____ I see?

car
dish
snake

Don't you _____ pizza?

miss
like
funny

We planted some _____.

books
fish
seeds

Many fish live in the _____.

pond
water
ocean

Your little sister is _____!

small
cute
sad

Skills: Recognizing long vowel sounds

PHONICS

Say each picture name.
Write the word under the picture.
Use the word bag to help you.

**ant   cat   fish
baby   tire   sun
stamp   bed
grass**

Skills: Recognition of vowel sounds; Word recognition

PHONICS

Two vowels, or a vowel plus w, that go together to make one sound are called **vowel digraphs**.
These vowel **digraphs** have special sounds.

Say each word below.
Do the two vowels work together to make one sound?
Underline the letters that make up each **vowel digraph**.

aw	oo
ea	au

book	pool	bread
spoon	school	thread
cook	auto	saw

Skills: Recognizing vowel digraphs

PHONICS

Each word in the box has a **vowel digraph**.
Write each word in one of the sentences below.

book   **school**
launch   **head**

I wore a cap on my _____.

I got a _____ from the library.

Rockets _____ the space shuttle.

She wasn't in _____ today.

Skills: Writing words that have vowel digraphs; Word comprehension

PHONICS

A **diphthong** is two vowels, or one vowel and the letter **w** or **y**, that mix together to create a special combined sound.

oi oy ou
ow ew

Look at each picture below.
Draw lines between the words that have the same diphthong.

oil   house

boy   clown

mouse   blew

down   coin

flew   toy

Skills: Recognizing diphthongs; Matching

PHONICS

Each word in the box has a **diphthong**.
Write one of the words in each sentence below.

down	**soil**
clown	**enjoy**

I saw a funny _____ at the circus.

We really _____ playing at the park.

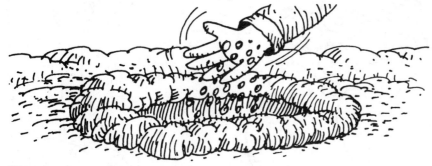

Plant seeds in the _____.

The elevator goes up and _____.

Skills: Writing words that have diphthongs; Word comprehension

PHONICS

The letters that are not vowels are called **consonants**.
Color in only spaces that have a **consonant** to find a surprise!

Skills: Recognizing consonants

PHONICS

Name each picture.
Circle the consonant whose sound you hear at the **beginning** of each word.

	b j z r d
	h z d m n
	b. k g c r
	m c a f d
	n u v t s
	s h r o k

Skills: Recognizing beginning consonant sounds

PHONICS

Circle the picture whose name **begins** with the sound of each letter.

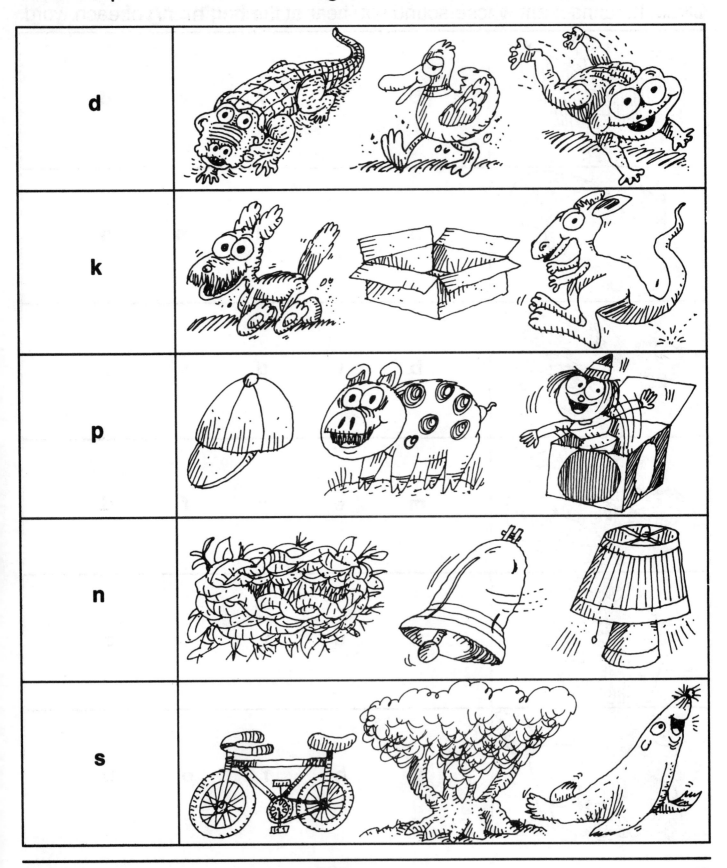

Skills: Recognizing beginning consonant sounds

PHONICS

Name each word.
Circle the consonant sound you hear in the **middle** of each word.

	k g z r d
	h z t m n
	b k d c l
	m v n f d
	k u z p s
	s l r o n

Skills: Recognizing medial consonant sounds

PHONICS

Name each picture.
Circle the consonant sound you hear at the **end** of each word.

	r n g m f
	d w m k g
	t d z k p
	v t h p r
	c l f t m
	p j l s n

Skills: Recognizing final consonant sounds

PHONICS

Say the name of each picture.
Listen for all the letter sounds.
Write the missing letter in each word.

__at

__ig

su__

p__n

__an

__ask

__ell

han__

c__p

__uck

ca__

__aw

Skills: Writing beginning and final consonant sounds

PHONICS

When **g** is followed by **a**, **o**, or **u**, it has the hard sound you hear in **gate**.
When it is followed by **e**, **i**, or **y**, it may have a soft sound, as in **gym**.

Say the name of each picture.
Circle it if it has a **soft** g sound.
Underline it if it has a **hard** g.

Skills: Understanding the soft g rule

PHONICS

When **c** is followed by **e**, **i**, or **y**, it has a soft sound, as in **face**.
Otherwise it has the hard sound you hear in **car**.

Say the name of each picture.
Circle it if it has a **soft** c sound.
Underline it if it has a **hard** c.

Skills: Understanding the soft c rule

PHONICS

A **consonant blend** is two or more letters whose sounds come together, but each letter's sound is still heard, as in the word **snap**.

Circle the **consonant blend** you hear at the beginning of each picture word.

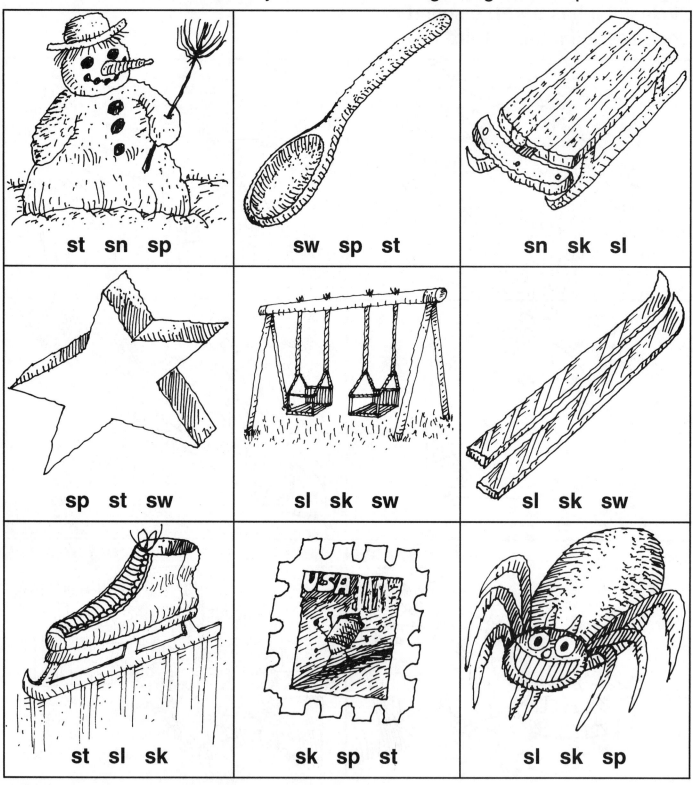

st   sn   sp

sw   sp   st

sn   sk   sl

sp   st   sw

sl   sk   sw

sl   sk   sw

st   sl   sk

sk   sp   st

sl   sk   sp

Skills: Consonant blends sk, sl, sn, sp, st, sw

PHONICS

Say the name of each picture. Circle the **consonant blend** you hear. Then write the word on the line. Use the word box to help you.

cloud	blocks	clock	flag	globe
flute	plant	flower	plane	

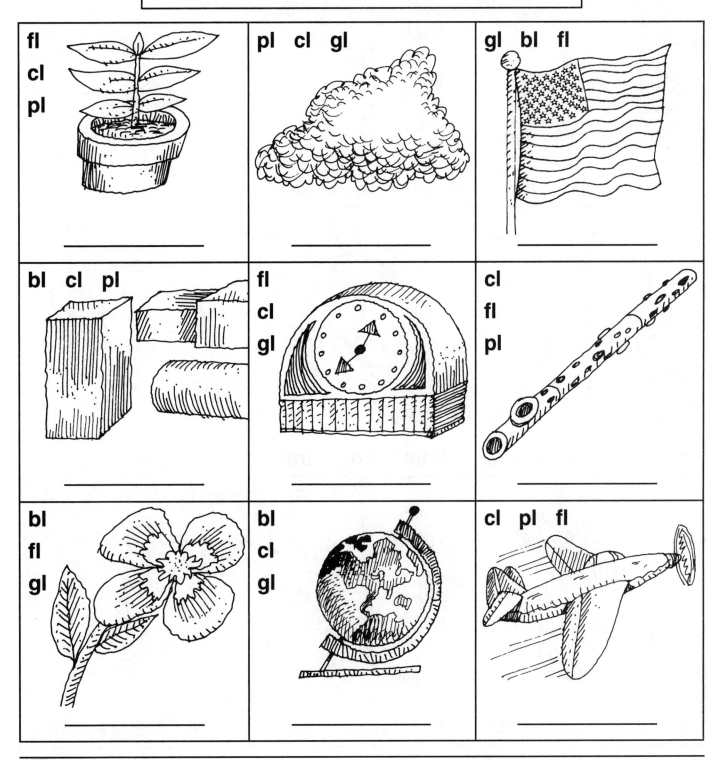

fl
cl
pl
_____

pl cl gl
_____

gl bl fl
_____

bl cl pl
_____

fl
cl
gl
_____

cl
fl
pl
_____

bl
fl
gl
_____

bl
cl
gl
_____

cl pl fl
_____

Skills: Consonant blends bl, cl, fl, gl, pl

33

PHONICS

Circle the word that names each picture.
What **consonant blend** do you hear at the **beginning** of the word?

trim train trip	dream drive drum	broom bright bridge
graph group grapes	from frog free	print price prince
drop dress drag	tray truck tree	break bridge brick

Skills: Consonant blends br, dr, gr, fr, pr, tr

PHONICS

Write the word that names each picture.
Use the word bag to help you.
Circle the **consonant blend** at the **end**
of each word.

stamp   belt   mask
raft   skunk   fish tank
lamp   plant   desk

Skills: Final consonant blends ft, lt, mp, nt, nk, sk

PHONICS

A **consonant digraph** is two consonants that together have just one sound, for example, **th** in **the**.
Look at the pictures in the box and say the name of each.

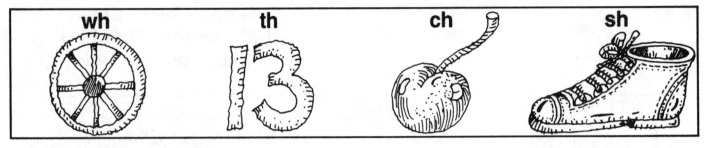

Now look at the pictures below. Say their names.
What **consonant digraph** do you hear at the beginning of each word?
Draw a line from the picture to that **consonant digraph**.

Skills: Recognizing the consonant digraphs wh, th, ch, sh

PHONICS

Some words may **end** with a **consonant digraph**, as in the word **fish**.
Name the picture on each fish.
Circle the consonant digraph you hear at the end of the word.

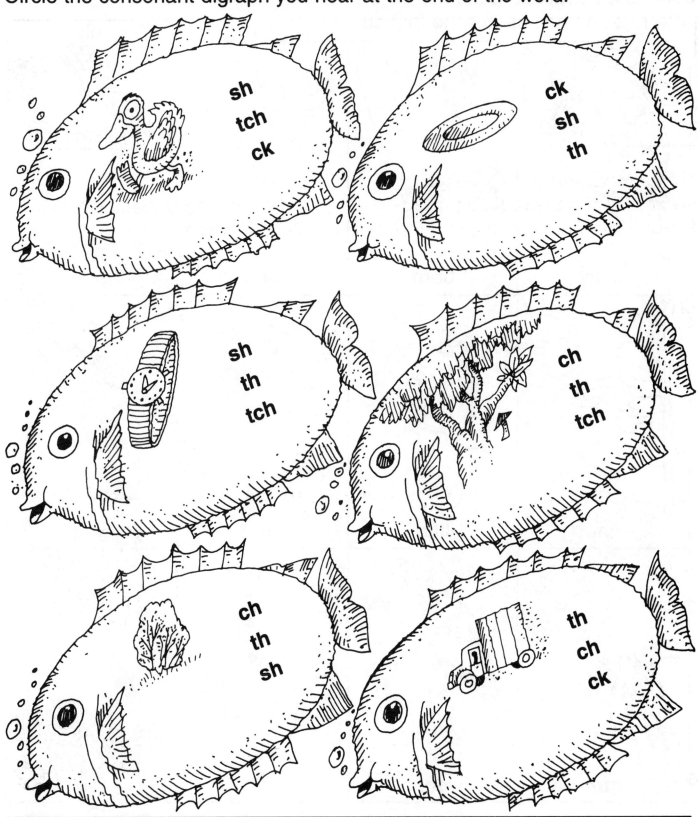

Skills: Recognizing the final consonant digraphs th, ch, sh, and tch

PHONICS

Name each picture. Look at the word below.
One consonant is wrong. Draw a line through it.
Write the correct consonant.
The first one has been done for you.

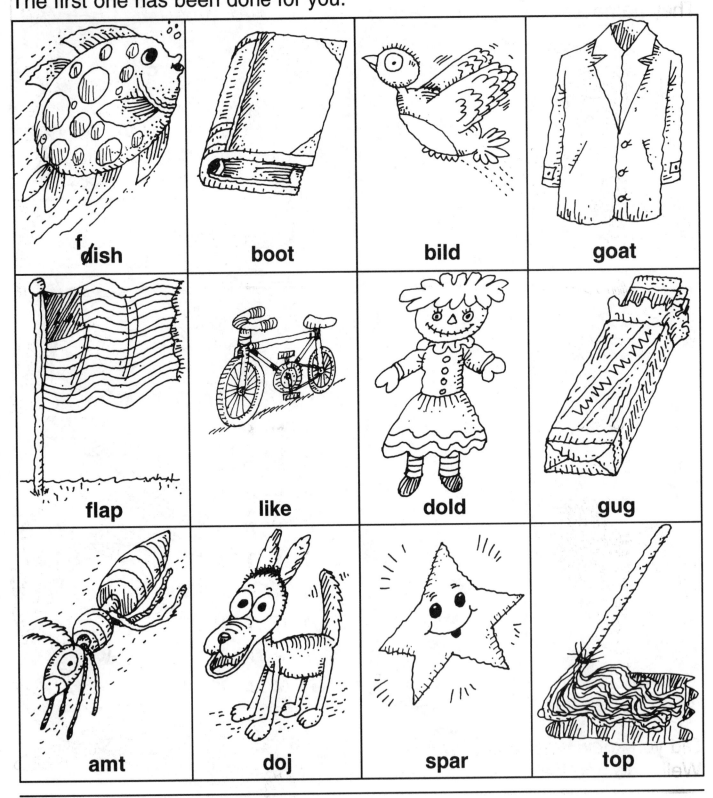

f d̸ish	boot	bild	goat
flap	like	dold	gug
amt	doj	spar	top

Skills: Recognizing consonant sounds

READING SKILLS

Find the hidden words below. Look across, down, and diagonally.
One has been found for you.
How are all the words alike?

They name _____.

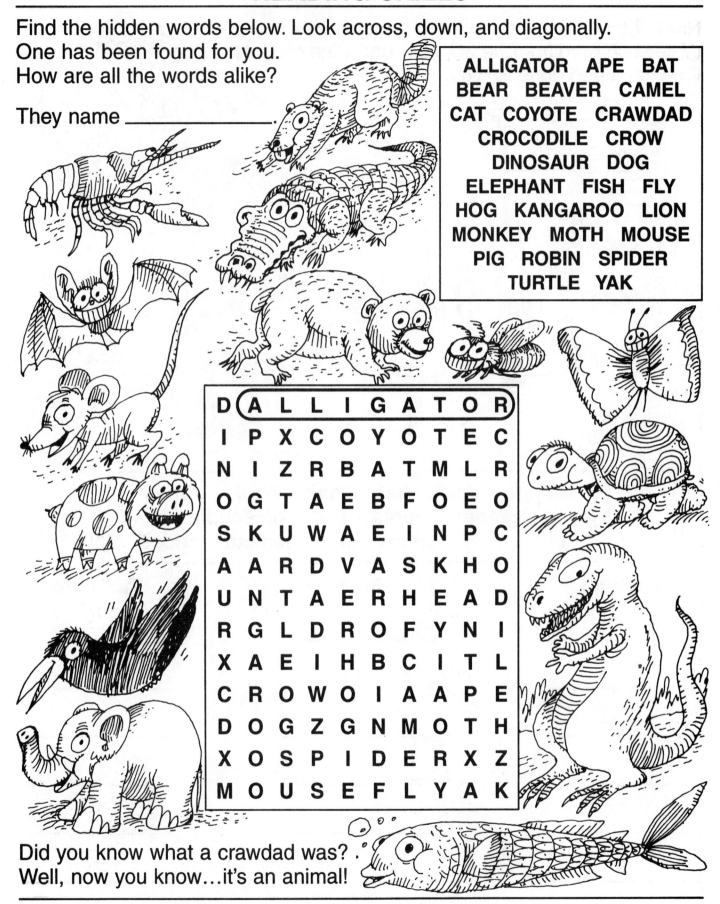

ALLIGATOR APE BAT
BEAR BEAVER CAMEL
CAT COYOTE CRAWDAD
CROCODILE CROW
DINOSAUR DOG
ELEPHANT FISH FLY
HOG KANGAROO LION
MONKEY MOTH MOUSE
PIG ROBIN SPIDER
TURTLE YAK

D	A	L	L	I	G	A	T	O	R
I	P	X	C	O	Y	O	T	E	C
N	I	Z	R	B	A	T	M	L	R
O	G	T	A	E	B	F	O	E	O
S	K	U	W	A	E	I	N	P	C
A	A	R	D	V	A	S	K	H	O
U	N	T	A	E	R	H	E	A	D
R	G	L	D	R	O	F	Y	N	I
X	A	E	I	H	B	C	I	T	L
C	R	O	W	O	I	A	A	P	E
D	O	G	Z	G	N	M	O	T	H
X	O	S	P	I	D	E	R	X	Z
M	O	U	S	E	F	L	Y	A	K

Did you know what a crawdad was?
Well, now you know…it's an animal!

Skills: Visual discrimination; Word recognition; Classifying

READING SKILLS

Read the headings of the three groups below.
Write each word from the word box under the correct heading.
One has been done for you.

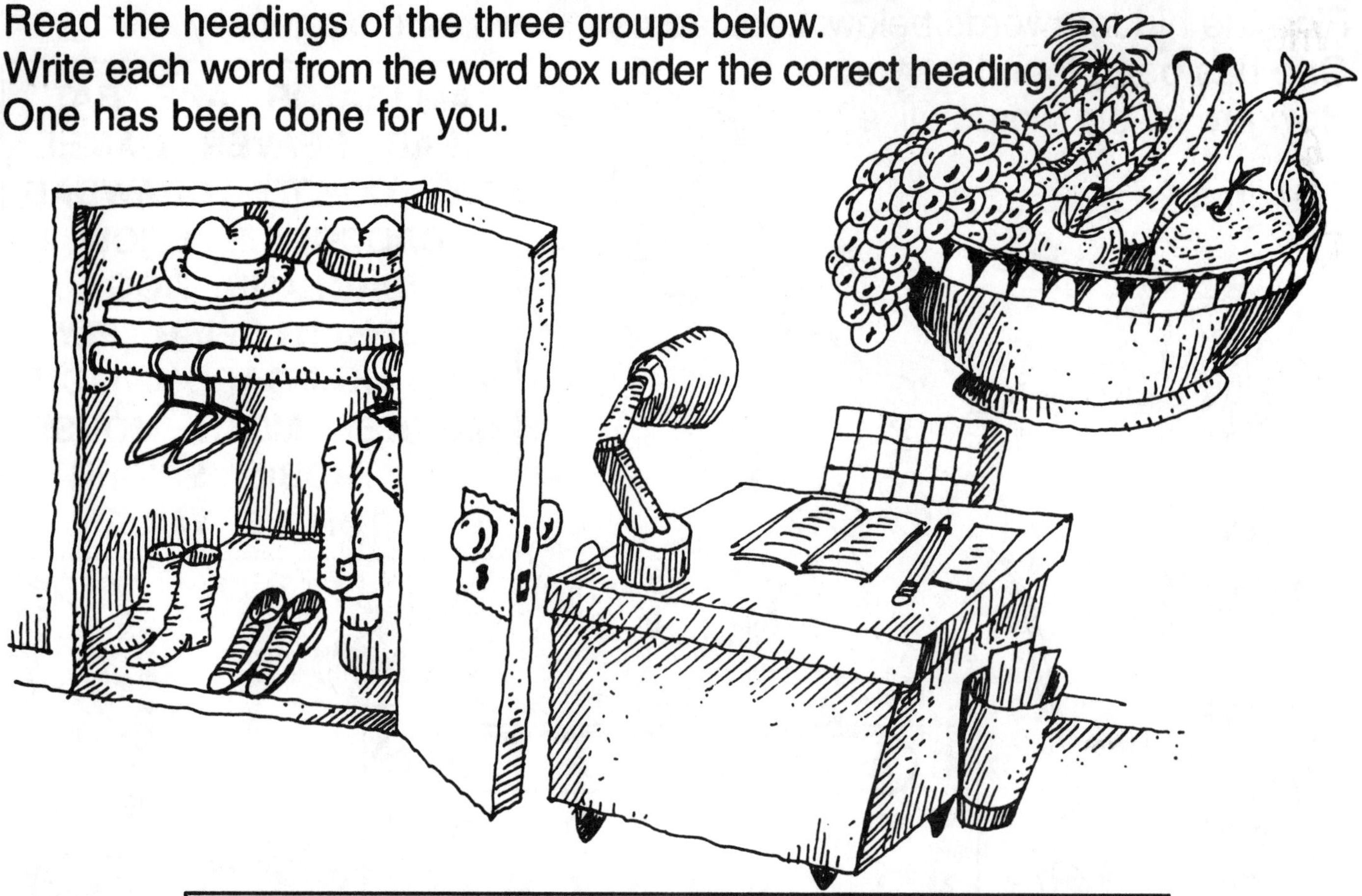

orange	desk	hat	chair	apple	dress
jeans	grapes	boots	bed	pineapple	sofa
lamp	pear	table	coat	banana	shoes

Clothing   **Fruit**   **Furniture**

orange

Skills: Classification

READING SKILLS

Write each word from the word box under the correct heading.

doll	mother	newspaper	teacher	train
magazine	top	doctor	kite	father
wagon	mail	baby	blocks	books

Toys   **People**   **Things to Read**

_____   _____   _____

_____   _____   _____

_____   _____   _____

_____   _____   _____

_____   _____   _____

Skills: Classification

READING SKILLS

Everything has a **cause** and an **effect**.
A clown slips on some soap. He falls down.
The soap is the **cause**.
His fall is the **effect**.

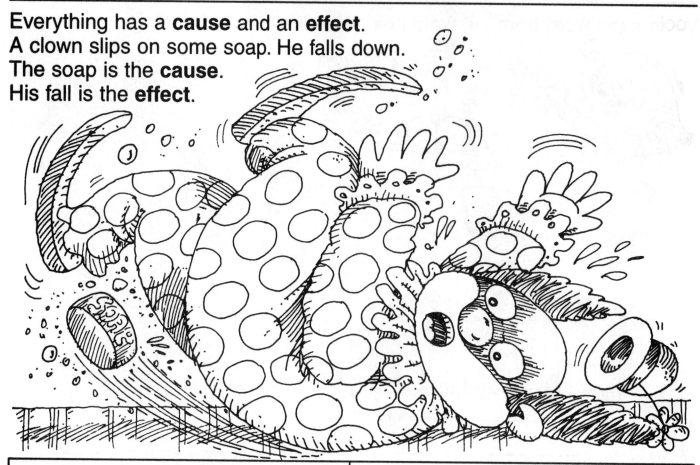

Cause	Effect
Read each problem. Make a ✓ in front of any likely cause.	Read each problem. Make a ✓ in front of any likely effect.
1. Andy doesn't have a dog because	1. We just moved to town, so I
—— he likes cats better.	—— go to a new school.
—— he likes to watch TV.	—— wear red shoes.
—— he has an allergy.	—— miss my old friends.
—— his mother won't buy one.	—— have a new house.
2. I'm going on the train because	2. We were hungry after school, so we
—— my grandpa lives far away.	—— fixed popcorn.
—— I like to skate.	—— had cookies and milk.
—— I have a ticket.	—— went to sleep.
—— a bear is in the circus.	—— asked mom for a snack.

Skills: Understanding the concept of cause and effect

READING SKILLS

Look at each picture. Circle the cause.

A bird popped the balloon.
A car ran over the balloon.
Racquel ate the balloon.

The dog drank the milk.
The baby spilled her milk.
Mother dropped a glass.

It is Thursday.
Maria is going to the beach.
It is starting to rain.

The wind knocked over our castle.
A big wave hit our castle.
A big bad wolf blew over our castle.

Now look at the picture below.
Draw what the effect will be.

Skills: Understanding the concept of cause and effect

43

READING SKILLS

Look at each picture.
Think about what is happening.
Then draw or write what you think will happen next.

Skills: Predicting outcomes

Read the story.
Think about what will happen next.
Draw a picture to show your prediction.

Robin and Kim were playing in the park.
"I'm getting tired," said Robin.
"Me, too," said Kim. "And I'm getting hungry."
"I wish I had a snack," Robin said.
"All I have is this banana," Kim said.

Skills: Predicting outcomes

READING SKILLS

Synonyms are words that have the same meaning, like **small** and **little**. You often find synonyms used in the stories you read.

Read the word in the middle.
Circle its synonym.

sad	silly
happy	
sleepy	glad

funny	yell
shout	
tall	slow

start	quit
stop	
loud	old

brave	fast
afraid	
like	scared

angry	tired
sleepy	
speedy	silly

Skills: Understanding synonyms

READING SKILLS

Antonyms are words that have the opposite meaning, like **big** and **little**.

Read each word in the middle.
Circle its antonym.

behind	out
above	
in	below

silly	sad
happy	
funny	cheerful

over	near
down	
close	up

young	old
new	
last	now

evening	moon
night	
noon	day

Skills: Understanding antonyms

READING SKILLS

Homonyms are words that sound alike but have different spellings and meanings, like **here** and **hear**.
Look for homonyms when you read.
Be careful with homonyms when you spell!

Look at the sets of **homonyms** in the word box.
Find and circle them in the puzzle.
Look across, down, and diagonally.

ATE	EIGHT
BE	BEE
THEIR	THERE
HERE	HEAR
RIGHT	WRITE
TO	TWO
NO	KNOW
WON	ONE
SO	SEW
THREW	THROUGH
DEAR	DEER
BLUE	BLEW
STARE	STAIR
SEE	SEA
CHEWS	CHOOSE
FOUR	FOR
SON	SUN

```
X T H R O U G H Z S K
C H O O S E A T E T N
H R B E E I G H T A O
E E B L E W D E E R W
W W H E U D E A R E S
S T H E R E W R I T E
S T A I R N W O N W W
O F O U R E O N E O Z
R I G H T X T H E I R
S U N J F O R X S O N
```

Skills: Understanding homonyms

48

READING SKILLS

Look for words like **first**, **next**, **then**, and **last** when you read. These words help you know the order, or **sequence**, in which things happened.

Read each sentence about a nursery rhyme.
Write numbers to show the order in which things happened in each story.

_____ Humpty Dumpty had a great fall.

_____ Humpty Dumpty sat on a wall.

_____ They couldn't put Humpty together again.

_____ All the king's horses and men came to help.

_____ The spider climbed the spout again.

_____ The eensy-weensy spider went up the water spout.

_____ Up came the sun and dried up all the rain.

_____ Down came the rain and washed the spider out.

Skills: Understanding sequence of events

READING SKILLS

Knowing the sequence of a story can help you make a **story map**. The story map will help you remember the story better.

Complete this story map.
Write the name of the story.

Story Title	
Characters	Jack The golden goose His mother The giant
Important Events	1. Mother sent Jack to sell the cow. 2. He traded her for magic beans. 3. The beans grew into a tall beanstalk. 4. Jack climbed the beanstalk. 5. Jack took the giant's golden goose.
Ending	Jack chopped down the beanstalk and killed the giant.

Skills: Understanding story order/making a story map

READING SKILLS

Look at the picture.
Complete the **story map** about that story.

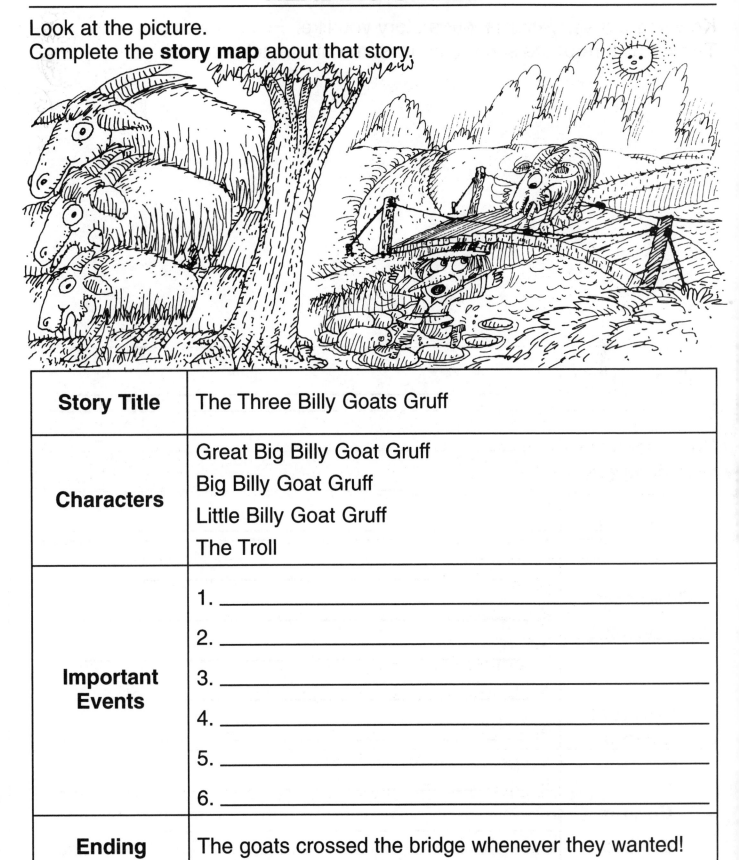

Story Title	The Three Billy Goats Gruff
Characters	Great Big Billy Goat Gruff Big Billy Goat Gruff Little Billy Goat Gruff The Troll
Important Events	1. _____ 2. _____ 3. _____ 4. _____ 5. _____ 6. _____
Ending	The goats crossed the bridge whenever they wanted!

Skills: Understanding story order/making a story map

READING SKILLS

Now make a story map about a story you like.
Draw a picture of the story to show some of the action.

Story Title	
Characters	
Important Events	1. _____ 2. _____ 3. _____ 4. _____ 5. _____
Ending	

Skills: Making a story map

READING SKILLS

A **character web** lists words that describe a person, or **character**, in a story.

Read this **character web** about someone in a familiar story.

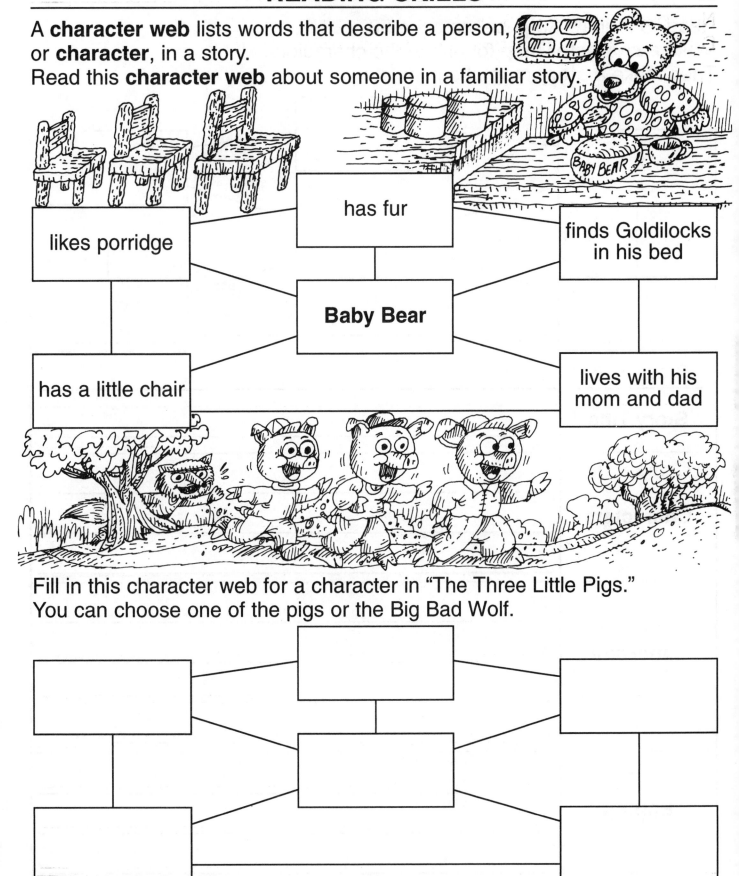

Fill in this character web for a character in "The Three Little Pigs."
You can choose one of the pigs or the Big Bad Wolf.

Skills: Making a character web

READING SKILLS

Read "Sabrina's Surprise" on page 58.
Make a **character map** for one of the characters.
Then make a **story map** about the story.

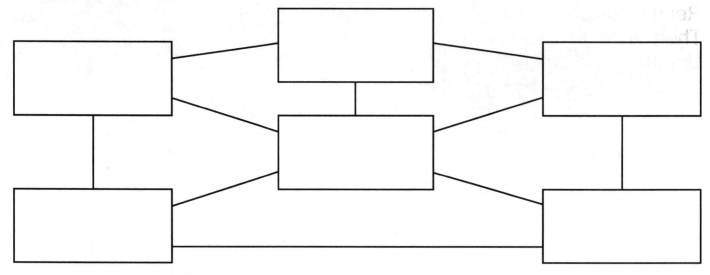

Story Title	
Characters	
Important Events	1. 2. 3. 4.
Ending	

Skills: Making a character web and story map

READING SKILLS

The **main idea** is what a story is about.
The other sentences give **details** that tell more about the main idea.

Read this story.
Then circle the **main idea**.
Underline the **details**.

Oil spills can harm animals. Sometimes big ships spill oil into the ocean. Birds that swim in the water get oil in their feathers. They can't swim or fly. Some birds swallow the oil. Many birds die.

People want to help the birds. They try to clean off the oil. Some birds are saved.

Skills: Finding the main idea; Environmental science

READING SKILLS

Read this story. Then circle the **main idea**.
Underline the **details**.

We should respect our flag. It is a symbol of America. We stand when the flag goes by in a parade. Why? We show others that we respect our country. We say the *Pledge of Allegiance* to show our respect for our country, too. Do you know all the words to the *Pledge of Allegiance*? Do you know what the words mean?

FOR A CHALLENGE:
Can you name any other symbols of America?
Try to list at least two more.

_____   _____

Skills: Finding the main idea and supporting details; Citizenship

READING SKILLS

Read about each story.
Circle the book cover that best shows the main idea of that story.

The story tells how a baby duck hatches from an egg.	EGGS AND DUCKS TURTLES FEEDING BIRDS
The story shows how to paddle a canoe and tie ropes.	BUS SAFETY KITE SAFETY BOAT SAFETY
The story tells about whales.	LAND GIANTS THE OCEAN GIANTS IN THE SEA

FOR A CHALLENGE:
Draw a book cover to show the main idea for a book about owls.

Skills: Finding the main idea

READING SKILLS

Sabrina's Surprise

"Happy birthday, Sabrina," said Mother. Then she gave Sabrina a big box. It was wrapped in paper. A red bow sat on top of the box.

"What is it?" asked Sabrina. She tore off the bow. She tore off the paper. She pulled the top off the box and looked inside. Then she ran to give Mother a big hug!

"Oh, thank you," Sabrina cried. "It's red and shiny, just like the one on TV! Does it go click-clack, too? Please, may we put it on the track?"

Sabrina and her Mother took the toy out of the box. They put **all the** parts down on the floor. Then they played with it. What do you think it was?

Read each question. Circle the answer.

1. What was sitting on top of the box?

a card   a red bow   a green bow

2. Whose birthday was it?

Mother's   Sam's   Sabrina's

3. What did Sabrina give Mother?

a box   a hug   a bow

4. Which toy do you think Sabrina got for her birthday?

bike   bear   jump rope   doll   ice skates
pair of boots   train   wooden puzzle

5. Now underline the toy above you would most like to have.

Skills: Comprehension; Making inferences

READING SKILLS

Pets, Pets, Pets

"I have two cats," Chris told his teacher. "I feed them every day."

"That's good, Chris," said Miss Andrews. "Who else has a pet?"

"I have a hamster named Bucky," said Juan. "His teeth stick out."

"And I have a dog named Misty," said Pat. "She's going to have puppies."

"I have a pet, too," said Miss Andrews. "It sings and swings in a cage. Can you guess what it is?"

Read each question. Circle your answer.

1. What kind of pet does Juan have?

2. What kind of pet does Chris have?

3. What kind of pet does Pat have?

4. What kind of pet does Miss Andrews have?

5. What kind of pet do you have or wish you had? _____

Skills: Recalling facts and drawing conclusions

Recycle!

We throw away tons of trash each year. Now Earth is running out of places to put the trash. So we need to make less trash!

Recycle to help to reduce trash. Old newspapers, plastic, cans, and glass can be made into new things. Old paper can be used to make new cereal boxes, greeting cards, and paper towels. Old plastic bottles can be used to make new plastic furniture. And old glass can be used to repair streets!

You can help. Get your family's old papers, cans, and bottles ready for recycling. And look for things made from, or packaged in, recycled paper when you shop.

Circle the word that best completes each sentence.

1. Earth is running out of space for _____.

    schools   animals   trash

2. Old paper, plastic, cans, and glass can be _____.

    eaten   recycled   written

3. Old glass can be used for repairing _____.

    streets   stockings   clocks

4. Look for recycled things when you _____.

    sleep   swim   shop

Now write one thing you will do to help cut down on trash.

_____

Skills: Recalling facts; Making decisions; Environmental science

READING SKILLS

Animal Coverings

Different animals have different body coverings. The body coverings keep the animals warm and protect the bones inside.

Bears and bunnies have fur. So do dogs, cats, kangaroos, and lots of other animals. But only one kind of animal has feathers…a bird!

Fish have scales to protect their bodies. The scales of lizards and snakes protect them from the hot sun.

Turtles have hard bony shells. So do crabs, clams, and lobsters. The hard coverings protect the animals' soft bodies inside.

Draw a line from each animal to its body covering.

FUR   FEATHERS   SCALES   SHELLS

Skills: Recalling facts; Classification

READING SKILLS

SENSE-ational Animals

Sight helps most animals find food and spot danger. Hawks fly very high. But their sharp eyes spot prey far below on the ground!

Not all animals have two eyes. Many spiders have eight eyes. Scallops have eyes all around their shells. Crabs do have two eyes, but each eye works alone. So crabs see things differently!

Taste is important to tell animals if things are safe to eat. Did you know that butterflies and some other insects taste with their feet?

Touch is an important sense for moles that live underground. They feel their way with whiskers and little bumps on their snouts. Cats and mice also use whiskers to feel their way in the dark.

Circle the animal in each row that has **more than** two eyes.

Now write **T** in front of a true sentence. Write **N** if it is not true.

_____ 1. Moles need the sense of touch to get around.

_____ 2. Butterflies taste with their feet.

_____ 3. Flies taste with their eyes.

_____ 4. Mice use whiskers to feel in the dark.

Skills: Recalling details

READING SKILLS

What Color Were Dinosaurs?

Only dinosaurs know what color they were…and they're not talking! Some scientists use **if–then** thinking to decide what colors dinosaurs may have been.

"**If** dinosaurs were lizard-like," said scientists, "**then** they must have looked like today's lizards. If today's lizards are brown, gray, or green, then dinosaurs must have been brown, gray, or green!"

Some scientists say dinosaurs were more like birds than reptiles. "So **if** dinosaurs were like birds," these scientists say, "**then** they must have had bright colors, like parrots and some other birds!"

One dinosaur expert says, "Colors? Your guess is as good as mine!" So color these dinosaurs the way you think they looked. Your guess is as good as anyone else's!

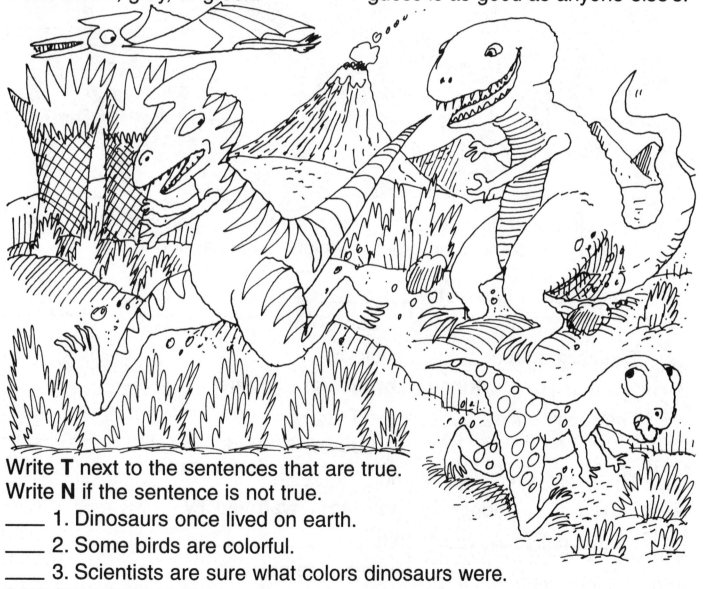

Write **T** next to the sentences that are true.
Write **N** if the sentence is not true.

____ 1. Dinosaurs once lived on earth.

____ 2. Some birds are colorful.

____ 3. Scientists are sure what colors dinosaurs were.

Skills: Decision making; If–then logic

READING SKILLS

No TV?

Carlos, Maria, and Max gulped down their breakfast. "Take your time!" scolded Mother.

"But it's Saturday," said Carlos. "Our favorite cartoons are on TV!"

Maria turned on the TV. "Mom!" she cried. "The TV doesn't work!"

Mother called the TV repair shop. "What will we do without TV?" the three kids sighed.

"You'll think of something," said Mother.

The kids thought. "Remember that game we got last Christmas?" said Carlos. "Let's play that!"

"Later," said Max, "let's paint!"

After lunch Mother said, "The TV is fixed. You can watch it now."

"No thanks, Mom," said the kids. "We've got other fun stuff to do!"

Circle the word that best completes each sentence. Then write **1, 2, 3, 4,** or **5** in each box to show the order in which things happened.

☐ Maria tried to turn on the _____ .

        stove   **computer**   **TV**

☐ The children ate _____ quickly.

        lunch   **breakfast**   **dinner**

☐ The repair shop _____ the TV.

        broke   **bought**   **fixed**

☐ The kids played a game and _____ .

        napped   **painted**   **watched TV**

☐ Mother called the repair shop on the _____ .

        TV   **cooker**   **telephone**

Skills: Recalling facts; Sequencing; Making inferences

READING SKILLS

Two Friends

Ginny and Mark are best friends. They are both second graders at Greenbay School. Mark is in Miss Murray's class. Ginny is in Mr. Howard's class. The two classes have music together on Fridays. Both Mark and Ginny like music.

Mark is a good tumbler, so gym class is his favorite. Ginny is a good artist, so art class is her favorite. Both kids like going to the library. Ginny's class goes on Tuesdays. Mark's class goes on Wednesdays.

Ginny and Mark walk to school together. They walk home together, too. So they spend a lot of time together. Do you spend a lot of time with your best friend?

> To **compare** two things, think of how they are alike.
> To **contrast** two things, think of how they are different.

Read each item.
Make an **X** in a column to show "Yes."
One has been done for you.

Alike or Different?	Ginny	Mark
Is a second grader	X	X
Is in Miss Murray's class		
Is in Mr. Howard's class		
Has music on Fridays		
Likes gym best		
Likes art class best		
Goes to the library on Tuesdays		
Goes to the library on Wednesdays		
Has a best friend in Greenbay School		

Skills: Comparing and contrasting; Recalling details

READING SKILLS

Groundhog Day

February second is Groundhog Day. That's when many groundhogs wake up from their winter sleep. The furry groundhogs creep out from their underground homes. They want to see if spring has come.

People say if a groundhog sees its shadow, it pops back underground. Then winter lasts six more weeks. If the groundhog doesn't see its shadow, spring soon comes. Do you think that's really true?

Circle the word or words that best complete each sentence.

1. Groundhogs live _____ .

   in the ocean   in caves   underground

2. Groundhogs are covered with _____ .

   scales   fur   feathers

3. Groundhogs are afraid of their _____ .

   food   leaf   shadows

4. Groundhogs want _____ to come.

   spring   winter   turtles

5. Groundhogs sleep in the _____ .

   rainbow   dark   water

Skills: Comprehension; Drawing conclusions

MATH

Fill in the missing numerals from 1 to 50.

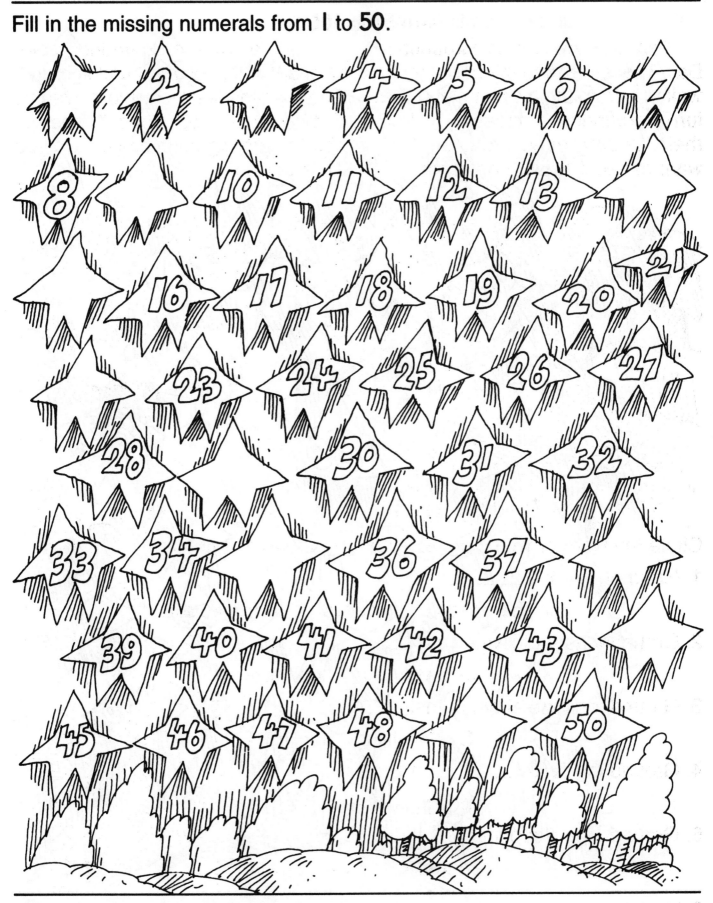

Skills: Visualizing and writing numerals 1-50

MATH

Fill in the missing numerals from **51** to **100**.

Skills: Visualizing and writing numerals 51-100

MATH

Count by **5**s. Fill in the missing numerals.

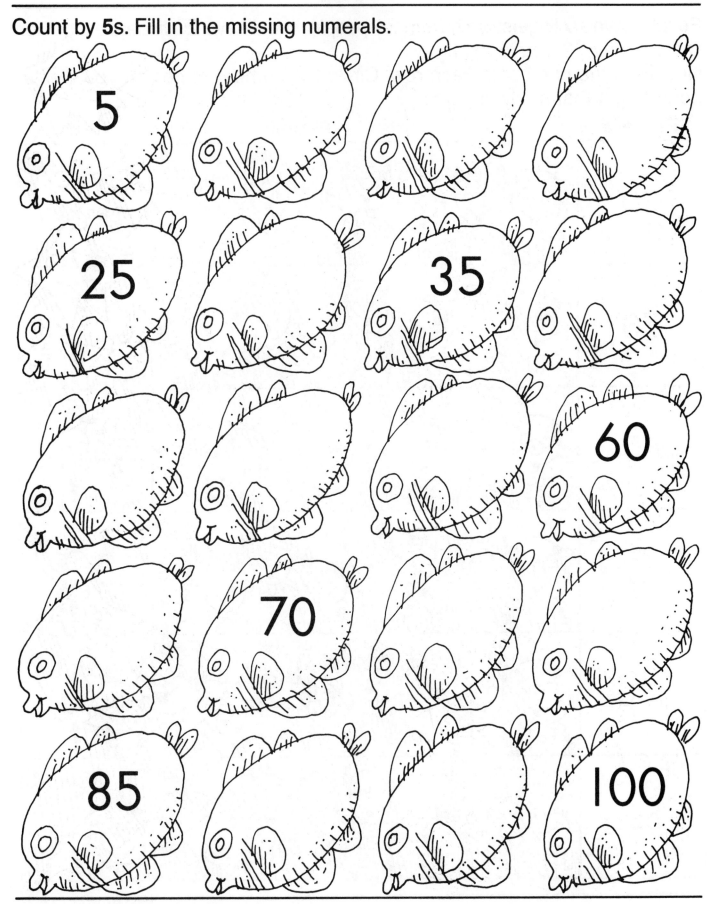

Skills: Counting by 5s; Writing numerals

MATH

People have **10** fingers. So how many people would have **20** fingers altogether? Did you say **2**? You're right!

Now read the number in each row. Circle the number of people you would need to get that many fingers.

Fingers	People
30	
70	
60	
10	
100	
50	

Skills: Counting by 10s

MATH

Circle 10 cookies. Then circle another group of 10 cookies.
Keep going until you run out of cookies.
How many groups or sets of 10 did you circle? _____

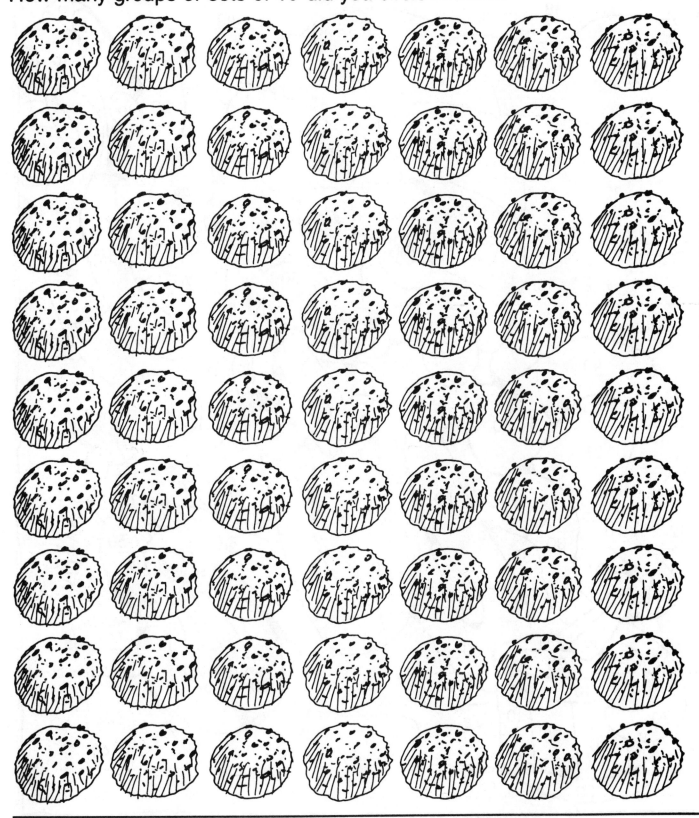

Skills: Counting by 10s

MATH

When you count by 10s, numbers always end in 0.
Color only numbers that end in 0 to see a music maker.

Skills: Counting by 10s

MATH

Start on **2**. Then count by **2**s as you follow the dots to **60**.
What do you see?

2   4
60 • •   •
58 •   • 6

•   • 8
• 10

56 •

12   14
•   •   • 16

• 18

54 •

20
•   • 22

52 •   • 24

• 26

30
•   • 28

46 •   32
44 •   38 •
40 • •   34
48 •   42   36

50 •

Skills: Counting by 2s

73

MATH

Some numbers are **even numbers**. Some numbers are **odd numbers**.
For **even** numbers, you start at 0 and count by 2s like this: 2, 4, 6, and so on.
For **odd** numbers, you start with 1 and count by 2s like this: 1, 3, 5, and so on.

Even	Odd	Even	Odd	Even	Odd	Even	Odd	Even	Odd	Even
0	1	2	3	4	5	6	7	8	9	10

Fill in the missing odd or even numbers.

4	6	8	____ ____
3	5	7	____ ____
14	12	10	____ ____
16	18	20	____ ____
13	11	9	____ ____
15	17	19	____ ____

Skills: Identifying odd and even numbers

MATH

Color all the spaces with **odd** numbers.

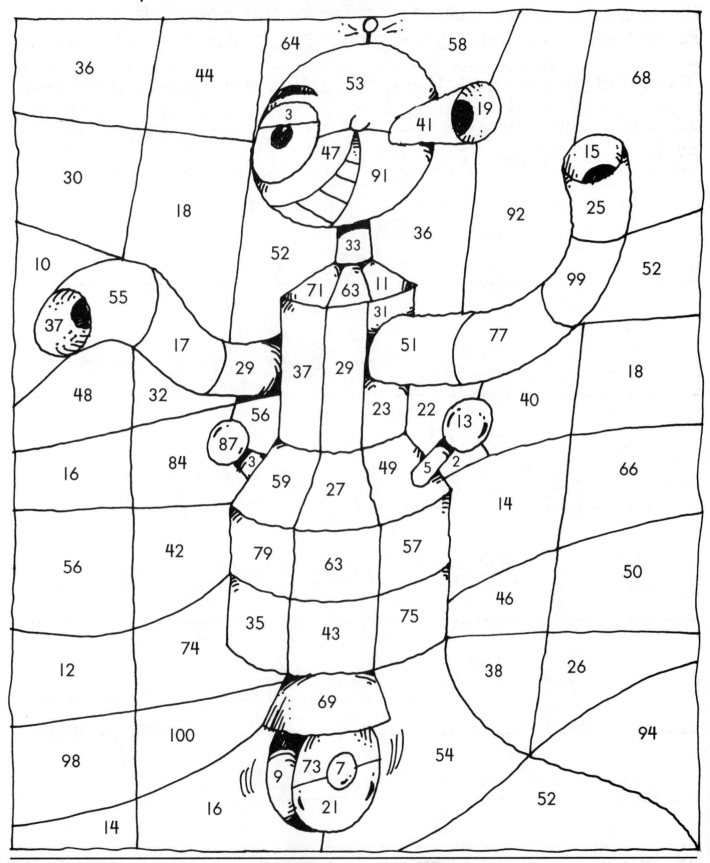

Skills: Identifying odd and even numbers

MATH

To count things in order, we use order words, or **ordinal numbers**. The ordinal number each clown is holding tells the clown's place in line.

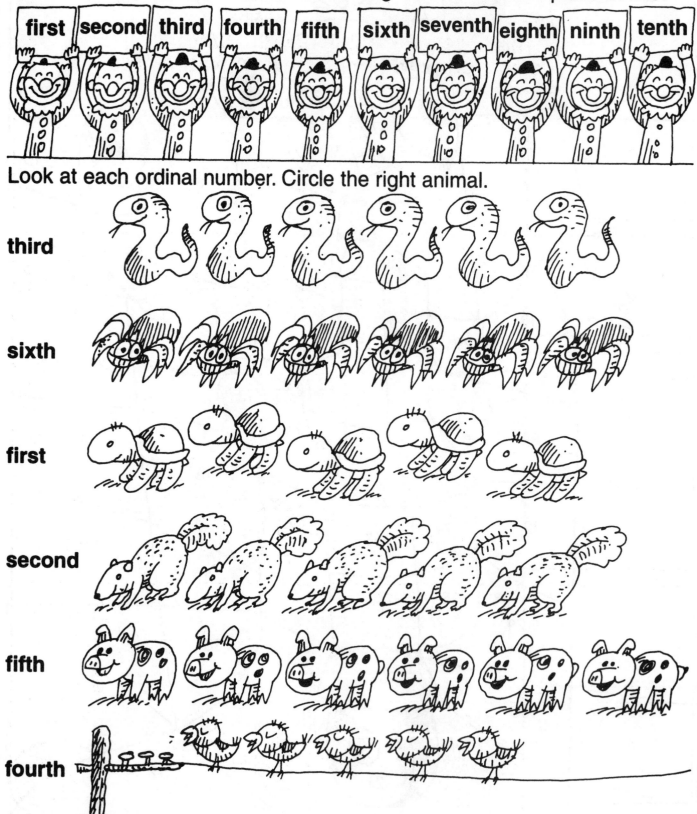

first   second   third   fourth   fifth   sixth   seventh   eighth   ninth   tenth

Look at each ordinal number. Circle the right animal.

third

sixth

first

second

fifth

fourth

Skills: Identifying ordinal positions

MATH

Look for the circled object in each row.
Write the correct **ordinal number** from the word box on the line.

first	second	third	fourth	fifth
sixth	seventh	eighth	ninth	tenth

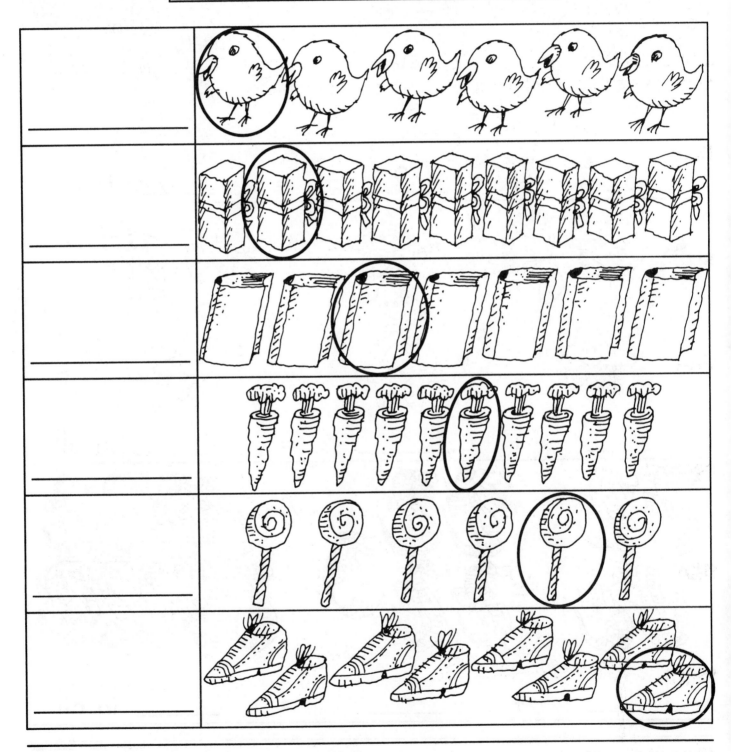

Skills: Identifying and writing ordinal numbers

MATH

Adding is putting numbers of things together.
Read the picture story problems. Write each equation.
The first one has been done for you.

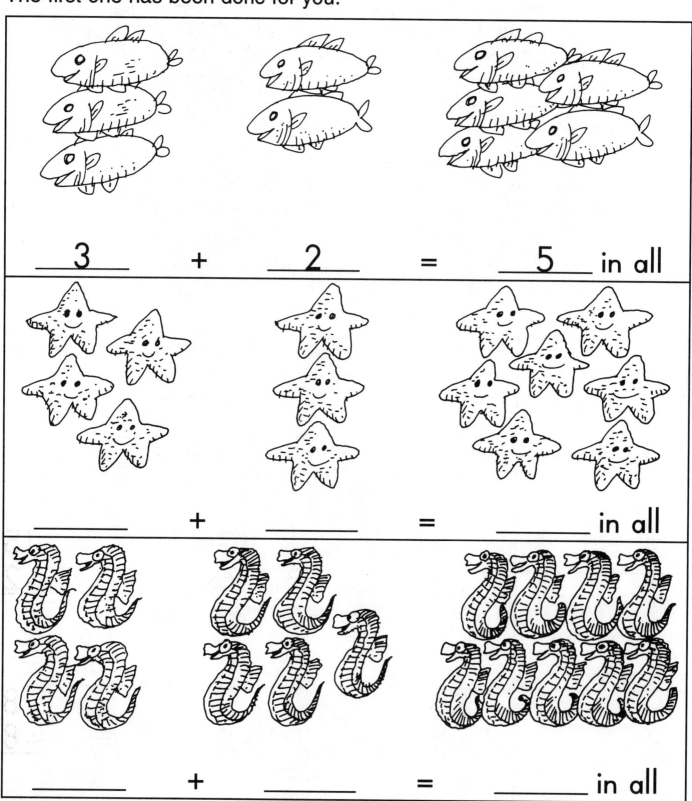

__3__ + __2__ = __5__ in all

____ + ____ = ____ in all

____ + ____ = ____ in all

Skills: Writing equations

MATH

Adding is putting numbers of things together.
Add the numbers below.

$2 + 2 = \underline{4}$ $2 + 3 = \underline{}$

$3 + 5 = \underline{}$ $6 + 4 = \underline{}$

$7 + 1 = \underline{}$ $5 + 9 = \underline{}$

$$\begin{array}{r} 3 \\ +4 \\ \hline \end{array} \qquad \begin{array}{r} 8 \\ +5 \\ \hline \end{array} \qquad \begin{array}{r} 10 \\ +6 \\ \hline \end{array} \qquad \begin{array}{r} 15 \\ +2 \\ \hline \end{array}$$

$$\begin{array}{r} 9 \\ +8 \\ \hline \end{array} \qquad \begin{array}{r} 6 \\ +5 \\ \hline \end{array} \qquad \begin{array}{r} 10 \\ +2 \\ \hline \end{array} \qquad \begin{array}{r} 8 \\ +8 \\ \hline \end{array}$$

Skills: Addition to two digits

MATH

Practice **regrouping**. Here's how:

		tens	ones
Add the **ones** first. 6 + 5 = 11 11 is 1 **ten** and 1 **ones**.	$\begin{array}{r} 16 \\ +15 \\ \hline 1 \end{array}$		
Give the 1 **ten** to the **tens**. Now add the **tens**.	$\begin{array}{r} +1 \\ 16 \\ +15 \\ \hline 31 \end{array}$	③	①

$\begin{array}{r} 44 \\ +17 \\ \hline \end{array}$

$\begin{array}{r} 56 \\ +28 \\ \hline \end{array}$

$\begin{array}{r} 27 \\ +36 \\ \hline \end{array}$

$\begin{array}{r} 31 \\ +39 \\ \hline \end{array}$

$\begin{array}{r} 62 \\ +19 \\ \hline \end{array}$

$\begin{array}{r} 16 \\ +38 \\ \hline \end{array}$

$\begin{array}{r} 12 \\ +38 \\ \hline \end{array}$

$\begin{array}{r} 45 \\ +29 \\ \hline \end{array}$

$\begin{array}{r} 39 \\ +12 \\ \hline \end{array}$

$\begin{array}{r} 22 \\ +59 \\ \hline \end{array}$

$\begin{array}{r} 42 \\ +49 \\ \hline \end{array}$

$\begin{array}{r} 17 \\ +38 \\ \hline \end{array}$

Skills: Two-digit addition with regrouping

MATH

Circle each wrong answer.

$$\begin{array}{r} 16 \\ +13 \\ \hline 28 \end{array} \quad \begin{array}{r} 32 \\ +32 \\ \hline 64 \end{array} \quad \begin{array}{r} 15 \\ +17 \\ \hline 32 \end{array} \quad \begin{array}{r} 22 \\ +18 \\ \hline 40 \end{array} \quad \begin{array}{r} 19 \\ +15 \\ \hline 34 \end{array}$$

Other problems:

$$\begin{array}{r} 29 \\ +13 \\ \hline 47 \end{array} \quad \begin{array}{r} 32 \\ +17 \\ \hline 49 \end{array} \quad \begin{array}{r} 28 \\ +36 \\ \hline 64 \end{array} \quad \begin{array}{r} 14 \\ +63 \\ \hline 75 \end{array} \quad \begin{array}{r} 11 \\ +86 \\ \hline 97 \end{array}$$

$$\begin{array}{r} 44 \\ +39 \\ \hline 83 \end{array} \quad \begin{array}{r} 50 \\ +18 \\ \hline 69 \end{array} \quad \begin{array}{r} 46 \\ +53 \\ \hline 99 \end{array} \quad \begin{array}{r} 20 \\ +63 \\ \hline 83 \end{array} \quad \begin{array}{r} 55 \\ +16 \\ \hline 71 \end{array}$$

$$\begin{array}{r} 48 \\ +43 \\ \hline 91 \end{array} \quad \begin{array}{r} 22 \\ +38 \\ \hline 66 \end{array} \quad \begin{array}{r} 39 \\ +26 \\ \hline 65 \end{array} \quad \begin{array}{r} 43 \\ +28 \\ \hline 72 \end{array} \quad \begin{array}{r} 19 \\ +68 \\ \hline 87 \end{array}$$

Skills: Practicing addition

MATH

Read each problem.
Draw a line to the correct answer.

39

$$\begin{array}{r} 43 \\ +18 \\ \hline \end{array}$$

91

$$\begin{array}{r} 22 \\ +17 \\ \hline \end{array}$$

$$\begin{array}{r} 62 \\ +29 \\ \hline \end{array}$$

26

52

$$\begin{array}{r} 13 \\ +13 \\ \hline \end{array}$$

$$\begin{array}{r} 15 \\ +37 \\ \hline \end{array}$$

97

$$\begin{array}{r} 56 \\ +14 \\ \hline \end{array}$$

61

$$\begin{array}{r} 78 \\ +19 \\ \hline \end{array}$$

$$\begin{array}{r} 12 \\ +68 \\ \hline \end{array}$$

70

80

Skills: Simple addition

82

MATH

To add more than two numbers, find the sum of the first two.
Then add that number to the next one, as shown below.

$$\begin{array}{r} 1 \\ +2 \\ +3 \\ \hline 6 \end{array}$$

$1 + 2 = 3$
Now add $3 + 3$.

$4 + 5 + 6 =$ _____ $6 + 7 + 5 =$ _____

$2 + 3 + 7 =$ _____ $9 + 2 + 1 =$ _____

$5 + 1 + 2 =$ _____ $3 + 3 + 3 =$ _____

$8 + 1 + 3 =$ _____ $4 + 2 + 1 =$ _____

Skills: Addition of multiple numbers

MATH

Who will win the race? Add the numbers in each lane.
The runner with the highest score wins!

Skills: Addition of multiple numbers

MATH

Subtracting is taking one number out of another.
Subtract the numbers below.

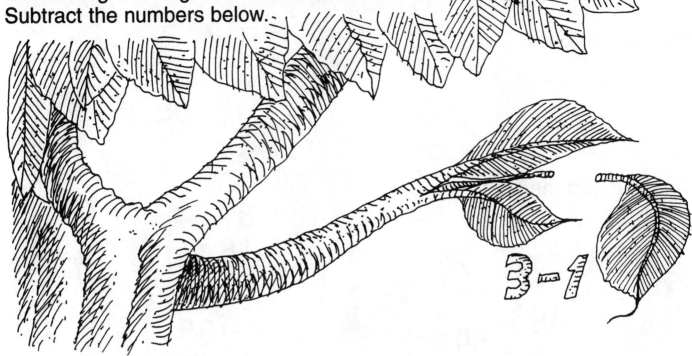

$3 - 1 = \underline{2}$ $3 - 2 = \underline{}$

$8 - 5 = \underline{}$ $7 - 4 = \underline{}$

$6 - 3 = \underline{}$ $10 - 2 = \underline{}$

$$\begin{array}{r} 4 \\ -3 \\ \hline \end{array} \qquad \begin{array}{r} 9 \\ -5 \\ \hline \end{array} \qquad \begin{array}{r} 7 \\ -2 \\ \hline \end{array} \qquad \begin{array}{r} 6 \\ -1 \\ \hline \end{array}$$

$$\begin{array}{r} 8 \\ -4 \\ \hline \end{array} \qquad \begin{array}{r} 8 \\ -2 \\ \hline \end{array} \qquad \begin{array}{r} 9 \\ -8 \\ \hline \end{array} \qquad \begin{array}{r} 9 \\ -9 \\ \hline \end{array}$$

Skills: Subtraction

MATH

Subtract the **ones**.

$$\begin{array}{r} 59 \\ -\ 5 \\ \hline 4 \end{array}$$

Then subtract the **tens**.

$$\begin{array}{r} 59 \\ -\ 5 \\ \hline 54 \end{array}$$

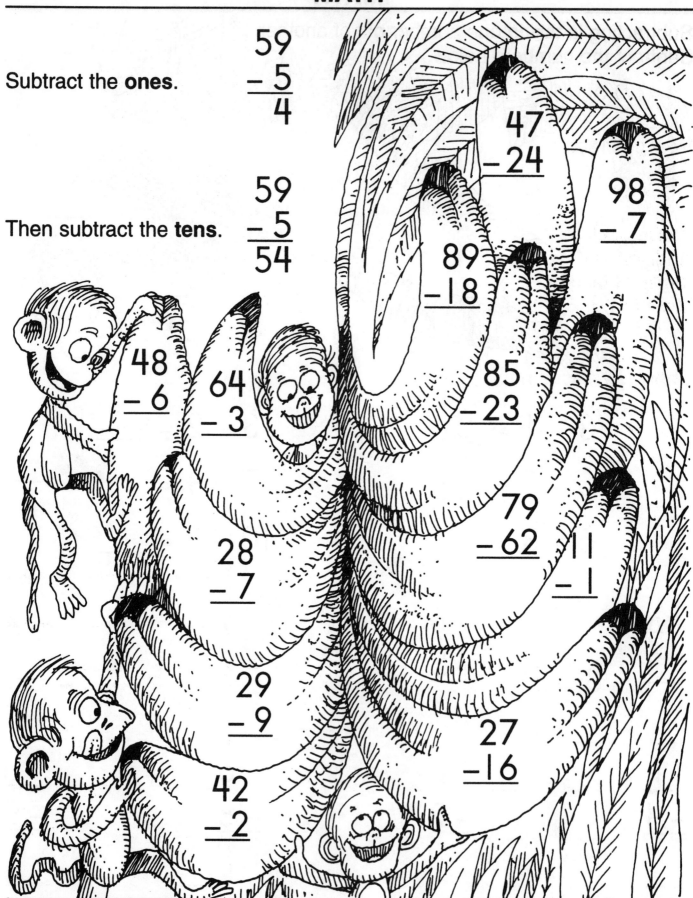

$$\begin{array}{r} 47 \\ -24 \\ \hline \end{array}$$

$$\begin{array}{r} 98 \\ -\ 7 \\ \hline \end{array}$$

$$\begin{array}{r} 89 \\ -18 \\ \hline \end{array}$$

$$\begin{array}{r} 85 \\ -23 \\ \hline \end{array}$$

$$\begin{array}{r} 48 \\ -\ 6 \\ \hline \end{array}$$

$$\begin{array}{r} 64 \\ -\ 3 \\ \hline \end{array}$$

$$\begin{array}{r} 79 \\ -62 \\ \hline \end{array}$$

$$\begin{array}{r} 11 \\ -\ 1 \\ \hline \end{array}$$

$$\begin{array}{r} 28 \\ -\ 7 \\ \hline \end{array}$$

$$\begin{array}{r} 29 \\ -\ 9 \\ \hline \end{array}$$

$$\begin{array}{r} 27 \\ -16 \\ \hline \end{array}$$

$$\begin{array}{r} 42 \\ -\ 2 \\ \hline \end{array}$$

Skills: Two-digit subtraction with no regrouping

MATH

Subtracting is the opposite of adding.
Begin with **3** apples. Add **2**.

$$3 + 2 = 5$$

Now subtract 2.

$$5 - 2 = 3$$

You're back to **3**.
Addition and subtraction sentences with the same numbers make up a family of facts.
Meet the **8, 6, 14 family**.

8+6=14	14−8=6
6+8=14	14−6=8

Show how these number families work.

7, 9, 16

7 + 9 = ___

9 + 7 = ___

16 − 9 = ___

16 − 7 = ___

5, 3, 8

5 + ___ = 8

3 + ___ = 8

8 − 5 = ___

___ − 3 = 5

6, 5, 11

___ + ___ = ___

___ + ___ = ___

___ − ___ = ___

___ − ___ = ___

7, 8, 15

___ + ___ = ___

___ + ___ = ___

___ − ___ = ___

___ − ___ = ___

5, 14, 19

___ + ___ = ___

___ + ___ = ___

___ − ___ = ___

___ − ___ = ___

9, 3, 12

___ + ___ = ___

___ + ___ = ___

___ − ___ = ___

___ − ___ = ___

Skills: Addition and subtraction facts

MATH

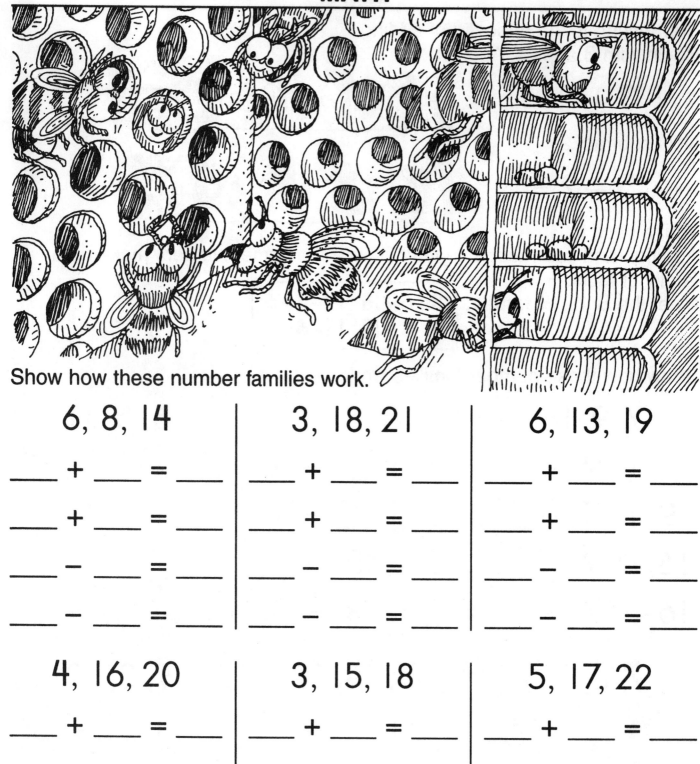

Show how these number families work.

6, 8, 14

___ + ___ = ___

___ + ___ = ___

___ - ___ = ___

___ - ___ = ___

3, 18, 21

___ + ___ = ___

___ + ___ = ___

___ - ___ = ___

___ - ___ = ___

6, 13, 19

___ + ___ = ___

___ + ___ = ___

___ - ___ = ___

___ - ___ = ___

4, 16, 20

___ + ___ = ___

___ + ___ = ___

___ - ___ = ___

___ - ___ = ___

3, 15, 18

___ + ___ = ___

___ + ___ = ___

___ - ___ = ___

___ - ___ = ___

5, 17, 22

___ + ___ = ___

___ + ___ = ___

___ - ___ = ___

___ - ___ = ___

Skills: Addition and subtraction facts

MATH

Subtract the numbers on each race car.
If the answer is **24**, color the car blue.
If the answer is **38**, color it red.
If the answer is **14**, color it yellow.

Skills: 2-digit subtraction with no regrouping

MATH

Circle each wrong answer.
Who had the most mistakes?

$$\begin{array}{r} 22 \\ -12 \\ \hline 10 \end{array}$$

$$\begin{array}{r} 54 \\ -32 \\ \hline 22 \end{array}$$

$$\begin{array}{r} 86 \\ -16 \\ \hline 71 \end{array}$$

$$\begin{array}{r} 92 \\ -11 \\ \hline 81 \end{array}$$

$$\begin{array}{r} 36 \\ -14 \\ \hline 22 \end{array}$$

$$\begin{array}{r} 49 \\ -37 \\ \hline 23 \end{array}$$

$$\begin{array}{r} 84 \\ -34 \\ \hline 50 \end{array}$$

$$\begin{array}{r} 91 \\ -79 \\ \hline 10 \end{array}$$

$$\begin{array}{r} 83 \\ -10 \\ \hline 70 \end{array}$$

$$\begin{array}{r} 73 \\ -21 \\ \hline 52 \end{array}$$

$$\begin{array}{r} 67 \\ -14 \\ \hline 54 \end{array}$$

$$\begin{array}{r} 85 \\ -13 \\ \hline 72 \end{array}$$

$$\begin{array}{r} 34 \\ -22 \\ \hline 12 \end{array}$$

$$\begin{array}{r} 74 \\ -11 \\ \hline 64 \end{array}$$

$$\begin{array}{r} 69 \\ -15 \\ \hline 55 \end{array}$$

$$\begin{array}{r} 55 \\ -24 \\ \hline 21 \end{array}$$

$$\begin{array}{r} 47 \\ -23 \\ \hline 24 \end{array}$$

$$\begin{array}{r} 68 \\ -16 \\ \hline 53 \end{array}$$

Skills: Recognizing subtraction errors

90

MATH

To subtract more than two numbers, find the difference between the first two numbers. Subtract the next number from that difference.

Who will win this race?
Every racer gets 99 points. But the racers want to get rid of the points.
Keep subtracting the numbers in each lane.
The runner with the lowest number of points wins!

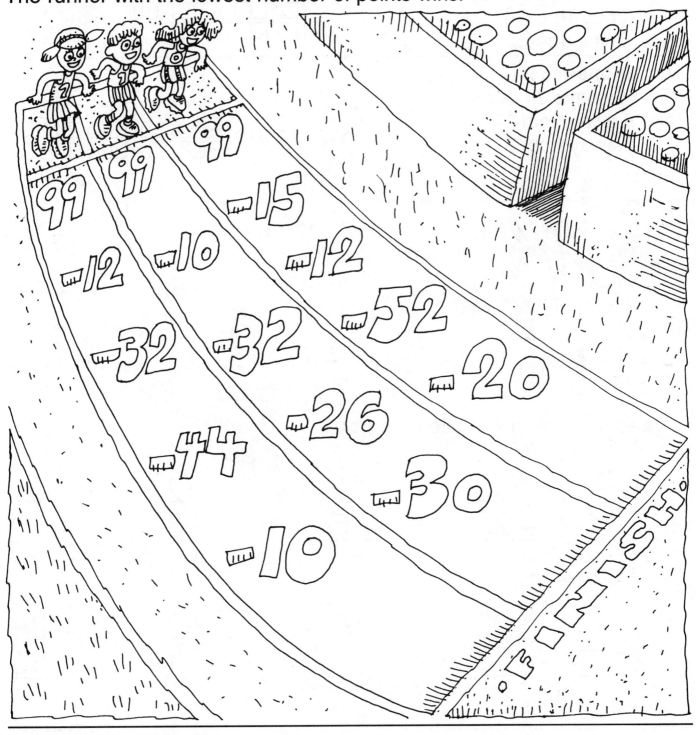

Skills: Subtraction of multiple numbers

MATH

Practice **regrouping**. Here's how:

		tens	ones
Subtract the **ones**: 4 – 5 **5** is bigger than **4**, so you can't subtract. First, **regroup** from the **tens**. Regroup **1 ten** from the **4 tens**. It becomes **10 ones**. That leaves **3 tens**.	$^3\cancel{4}^{+10}4$ -25	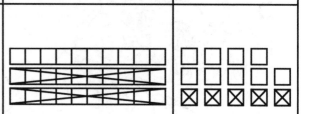	
Add **10 ones** to the **4**. Now you have **14 ones**. Take **5** away from **14**. Take **2** away from **3**.	$^3\cancel{4}^{14}\cancel{4}$ $\underline{-25}$ 19		

Solve each problem. Be sure to **regroup**.

$$\begin{array}{r} 74 \\ -37 \\ \hline \end{array} \qquad \begin{array}{r} 50 \\ -25 \\ \hline \end{array} \qquad \begin{array}{r} 86 \\ -17 \\ \hline \end{array} \qquad \begin{array}{r} 42 \\ -13 \\ \hline \end{array} \qquad \begin{array}{r} 31 \\ -9 \\ \hline \end{array}$$

$$\begin{array}{r} 65 \\ -27 \\ \hline \end{array} \qquad \begin{array}{r} 92 \\ -33 \\ \hline \end{array} \qquad \begin{array}{r} 71 \\ -18 \\ \hline \end{array} \qquad \begin{array}{r} 62 \\ -24 \\ \hline \end{array} \qquad \begin{array}{r} 84 \\ -46 \\ \hline \end{array}$$

Skills: Regrouping to solve 2-digit subtraction problems

MATH

Add or subtract the numbers below.

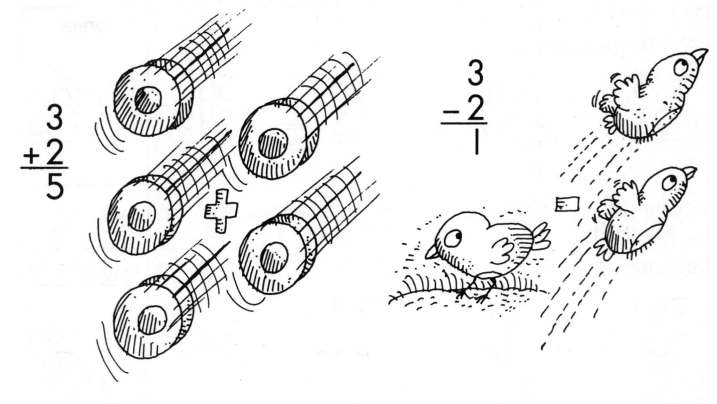

$$\begin{array}{r} 3 \\ +2 \\ \hline 5 \end{array}$$

$$\begin{array}{r} 3 \\ -2 \\ \hline 1 \end{array}$$

$$\begin{array}{r} 4 \\ +2 \\ \hline \end{array}$$
$$\begin{array}{r} 8 \\ +6 \\ \hline \end{array}$$
$$\begin{array}{r} 29 \\ +7 \\ \hline \end{array}$$
$$\begin{array}{r} 63 \\ -24 \\ \hline \end{array}$$
$$\begin{array}{r} 14 \\ -6 \\ \hline \end{array}$$

$$\begin{array}{r} 8 \\ +3 \\ \hline \end{array}$$
$$\begin{array}{r} 5 \\ +2 \\ \hline \end{array}$$
$$\begin{array}{r} 11 \\ +7 \\ \hline \end{array}$$
$$\begin{array}{r} 11 \\ -3 \\ \hline \end{array}$$
$$\begin{array}{r} 55 \\ +5 \\ \hline \end{array}$$

$$\begin{array}{r} 12 \\ +1 \\ \hline \end{array}$$
$$\begin{array}{r} 14 \\ -13 \\ \hline \end{array}$$
$$\begin{array}{r} 5 \\ +7 \\ \hline \end{array}$$
$$\begin{array}{r} 66 \\ +34 \\ \hline \end{array}$$
$$\begin{array}{r} 9 \\ -3 \\ \hline \end{array}$$

Skills: Adding and subtracting with and without regrouping

MATH

To add 3-digit numbers, add the **ones** first, then the **tens**, then the **hundreds**.

Solve the problems.

$$\begin{array}{r} 145 \\ + \ 23 \\ \hline \end{array} \qquad \begin{array}{r} 251 \\ + \ 48 \\ \hline \end{array} \qquad \begin{array}{r} 305 \\ +123 \\ \hline \end{array} \qquad \begin{array}{r} 500 \\ +232 \\ \hline \end{array} \qquad \begin{array}{r} 823 \\ +165 \\ \hline \end{array}$$

To subtract 3-digit numbers, subtract the **ones** first, then the **tens**, then the **hundreds**.

Solve the problems.

$$\begin{array}{r} 750 \\ -300 \\ \hline \end{array} \qquad \begin{array}{r} 387 \\ - \ 15 \\ \hline \end{array} \qquad \begin{array}{r} 923 \\ -322 \\ \hline \end{array} \qquad \begin{array}{r} 398 \\ -266 \\ \hline \end{array} \qquad \begin{array}{r} 434 \\ - \ 22 \\ \hline \end{array}$$

Skills: 3-digit addition and subtraction with no regrouping

MATH

Read the riddles below.
What do you need to do with the numbers?

Solve the riddles.

You'll get 9 if you add 5 to me.
Just what number can I be?

What number am I? _____

Take 3 away, then take 3 more,
And you'll have 3 to keep in store.

What number am I? _____

Take 4 away from me, now add 3,
Then add 2 more and 9 you'll see!

What number am I? _____

Add 5 to me and now add 3,
Now take away 1, and 8 I'll be!

What number am I? _____

Take 7 away from me, now add 4,
And you get 7—no less, no more!

What number am I? _____

Add 6 to me, then take away 5,
You'll have 15, and that's no jive!

What number am I? _____

Skills: Solving word problems

MATH

Read each question. Look at the picture. Write your answers.

How many sneakers are on the floor? _____

Draw 2 more sneakers. Now how many are there? _____

How many umbrellas do you see? _____

Cross out 2 umbrellas. Now how many are there? _____

How many boots do you see? _____

Draw 4 boots. Now how many are there? _____

How many socks do you see? _____

Cross out 4 socks. Now how many? _____

Skills: Solving word problems

MATH

Read each question. Look at the picture. Write your answers.

The balloon man had 8 balloons. He sold 2.
3 floated away. Now how many does he have? _____

Did you add or subtract? _____

The hot dog vendor sold 3 hot dogs.
Then 2 children came and each bought one. How many did he sell? _____

Did you add or subtract? _____

How many triangle flags do you see? _____
Draw 4 flags. Now how many are there? _____

Did you add or subtract? _____

There are 6 people on the ferris wheel.
There are 5 people on the merry-go-round.

How many people in all on rides? _____

Did you add or subtract? _____

Skills: Solving word problems

MATH

Read each story. Write the **equation**.

1. There are **215** kids in Bill's school.

   There are **110** boys in the school.

   How many girls go to Bill's school?

2. The cafeteria served **189** hot lunches on Monday.

   They served **176** lunches on Friday.

   How many fewer people ate lunch on Friday?

3. Our basketball team scored **42** points in the first half.

   The other team scored **67**.

   How many points do we need to catch up?

Skills: Solving word problems

MATH

Multiplying is a short cut to adding.
For instance, **3 x 2** means **3** groups of **2**, or **2 + 2 + 2**.

Look at the empty plates.
Draw cookies on each plate to show the multiplication problem.
Then solve the problem. The answer is called the **product**.

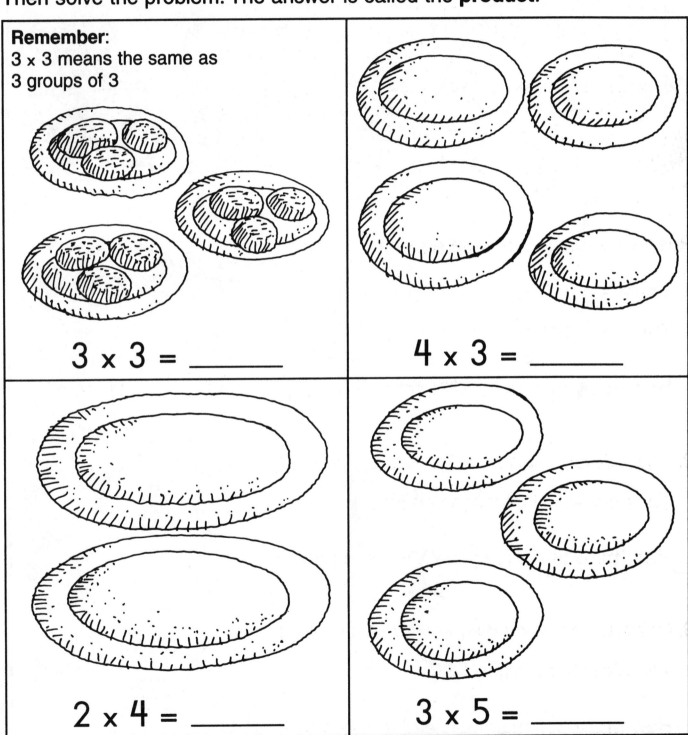

Remember:
3 x 3 means the same as
3 groups of 3

$3 \times 3 =$ _____

$4 \times 3 =$ _____

$2 \times 4 =$ _____

$3 \times 5 =$ _____

Skills: Understanding multiplication

MATH

Look at each multiplication problem.
Draw a line to match the problem with the picture that shows it.
Write the **product**.

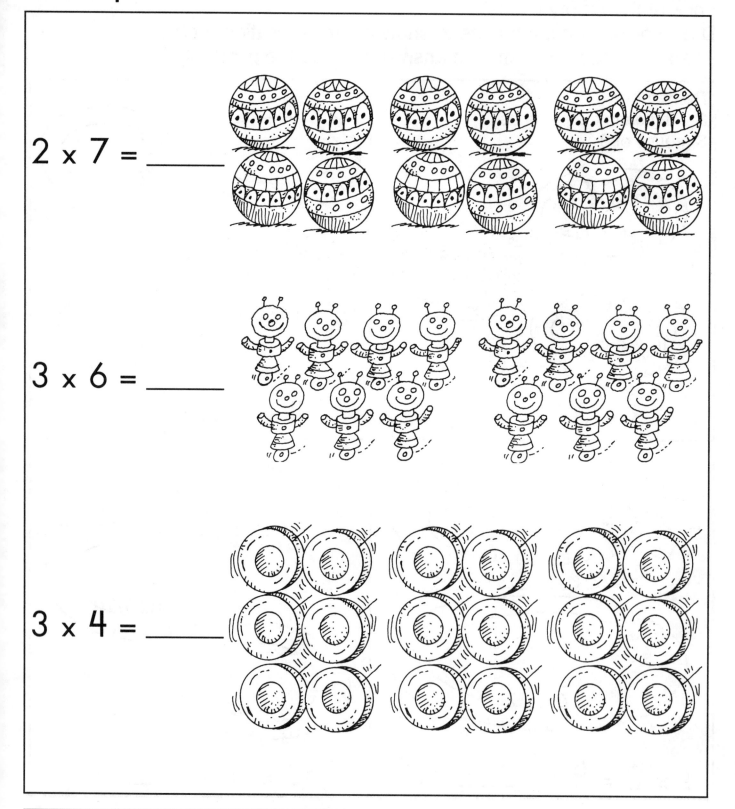

2 x 7 = _____

3 x 6 = _____

3 x 4 = _____

Skills: Understanding multiplication

MATH

Look at each multiplication problem.
Draw a picture to show the problem.
Write the **product**.

5 x 4 = _____

2 x 7 = _____

3 x 2 = _____

Skills: Understanding multiplication

MATH

Read each problem. Write the **product**.

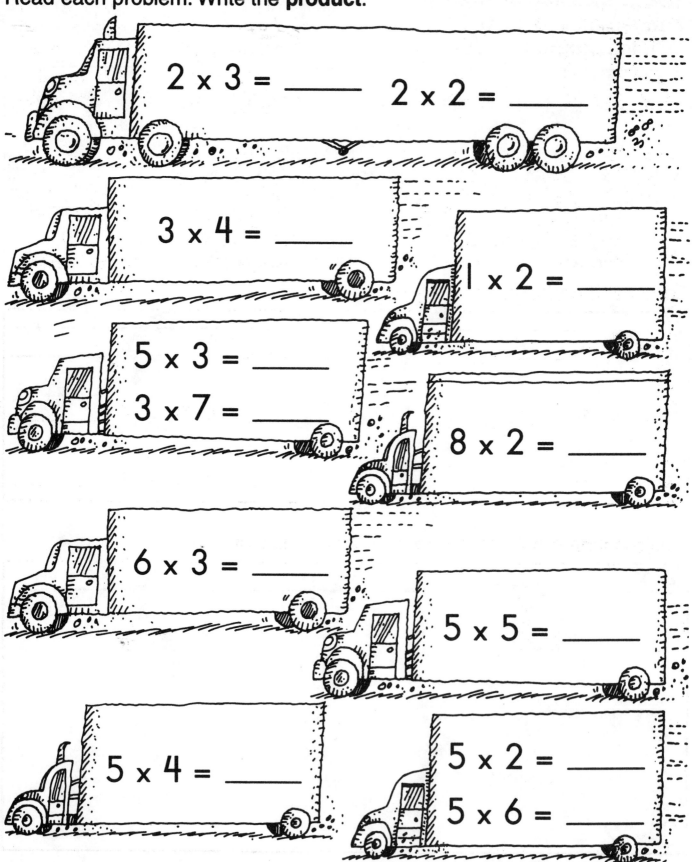

$2 \times 3 =$ _____ $2 \times 2 =$ _____

$3 \times 4 =$ _____

$1 \times 2 =$ _____

$5 \times 3 =$ _____
$3 \times 7 =$ _____

$8 \times 2 =$ _____

$6 \times 3 =$ _____

$5 \times 5 =$ _____

$5 \times 4 =$ _____

$5 \times 2 =$ _____

$5 \times 6 =$ _____

Skills: Multiplication of 2s, 3s, and 5s

Read each problem. Write the **product**.

2 x 4 = _____	5 x 2 = _____	6 x 2 = _____
4 x 10 = _____	7 x 5 = _____	10 x 3 = _____
2 x 7 = _____	6 x 5 = _____	4 x 3 = _____

Multiplication problems can also be written like this:

$$\begin{array}{r} 10 \\ \times 2 \\ \hline \end{array} \qquad \begin{array}{r} 5 \\ \times 1 \\ \hline \end{array} \qquad \begin{array}{r} 2 \\ \times 9 \\ \hline \end{array}$$

$$\begin{array}{r} 6 \\ \times 3 \\ \hline \end{array} \qquad \begin{array}{r} 9 \\ \times 3 \\ \hline \end{array} \qquad \begin{array}{r} 8 \\ \times 2 \\ \hline \end{array}$$

Skills: Solving vertical and horizontal multiplication problems

MATH

Write the missing words to complete this story about measuring.
Use the word box to help you spell the words.

```
inches   quarts   teaspoon
degrees   ounces   miles   gallon
```

We measure things every day. And we measure in many different ways. Maybe you've seen signs like these:

Gasoline   **To Chicago**

$1.20 a _____   110 _____

$1.20
GALLONS

CHICAGO
110 MILES

We measure gas by the gallon and distance by miles. We also measure

- temperature by _____.

- weight by pounds and _____.

- height by feet and _____.

- milk by pints and _____.

- spices by the _____.

Skills: Identifying and writing units of measure

MATH

Circle the tallest person or object.

Skills: Comparing height

MATH

Measuring is comparing sizes with a unit of measure.
If you don't have a ruler, you can use paper clips or buttons!

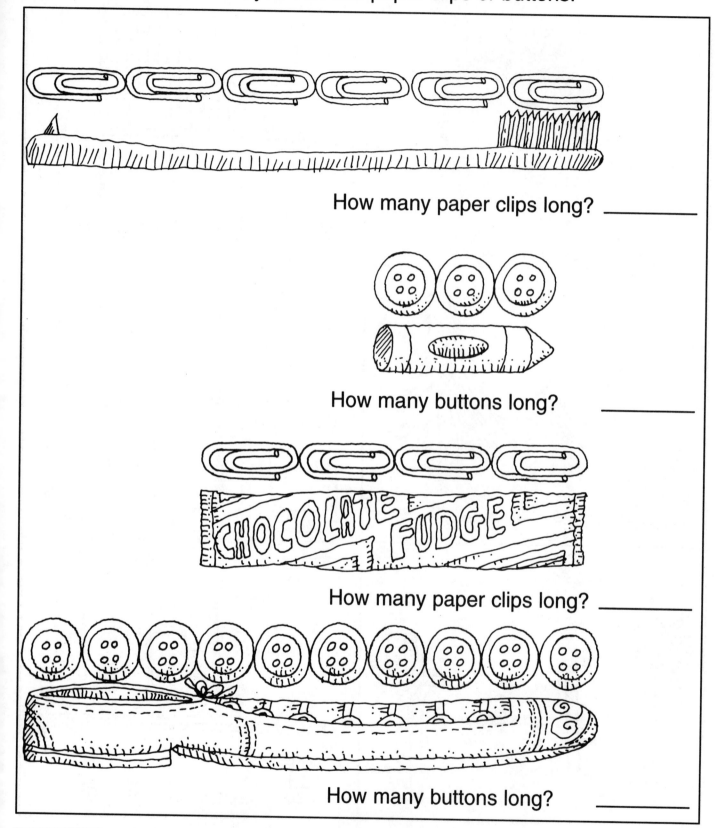

How many paper clips long? _____

How many buttons long? _____

How many paper clips long? _____

How many buttons long? _____

Skills: Measuring with non-standard units of measure

MATH

An **inch** is a standard unit of measure for length.
The numbers on rulers and tape measures show inches.

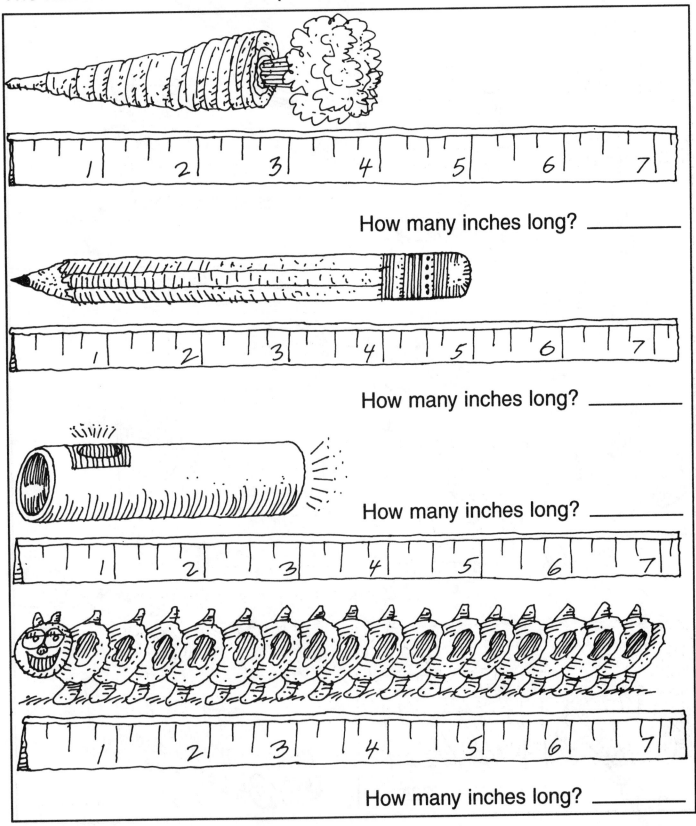

How many inches long? _____

How many inches long? _____

How many inches long? _____

How many inches long? _____

Skills: Measuring length by inches

MATH

Look at each picture. Circle the **heaviest** person or object.

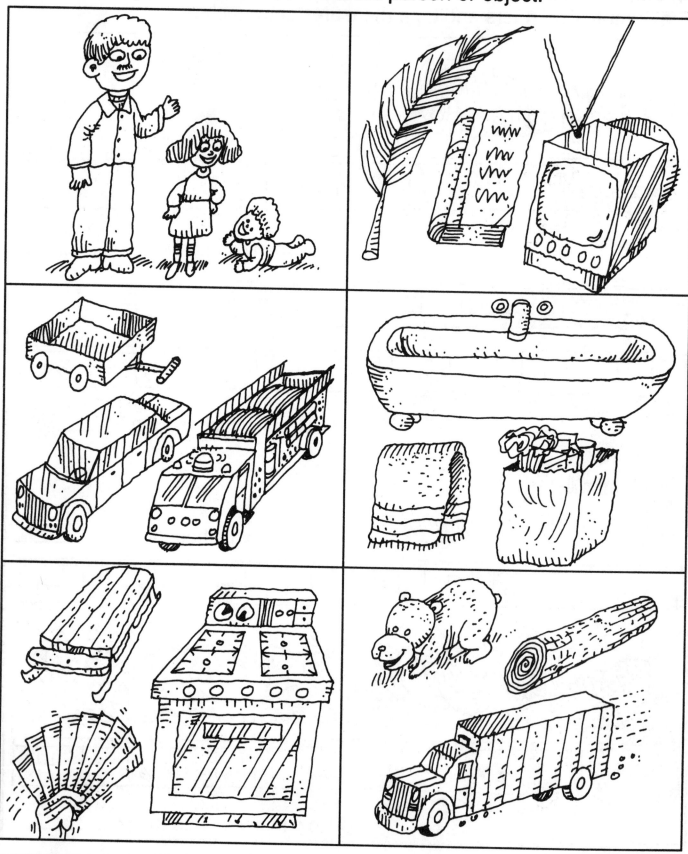

MATH

Look at each picture. Circle the object that holds the **most**.

Skills: Comparing volume or holding capacity

MATH

 1 quart   holds as much as   2 pints

 1 gallon   holds as much as   4 quarts

Circle the one or ones that hold more milk.

Skills: Comparing liquid volume

MATH

Coins are money.

A penny = one cent (1¢).

Count the pennies. How many?

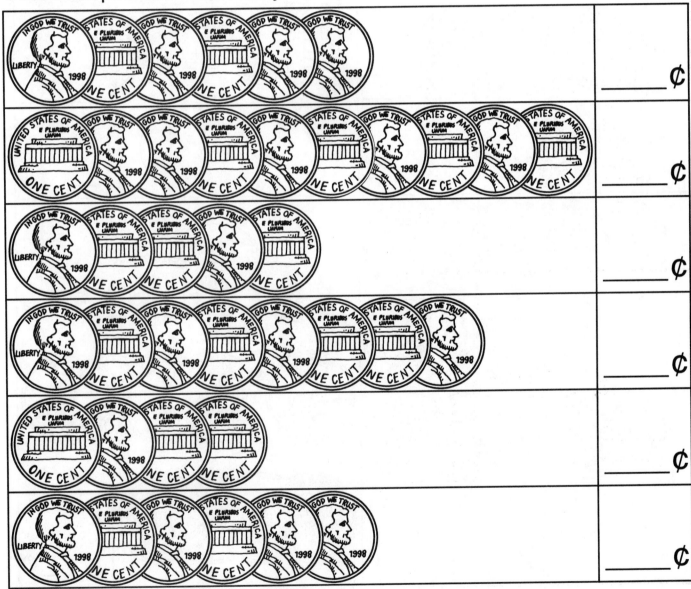

Skills: Counting and writing money values

MATH

How much does each thing cost?
Count the pennies.
Write the price on the tag.

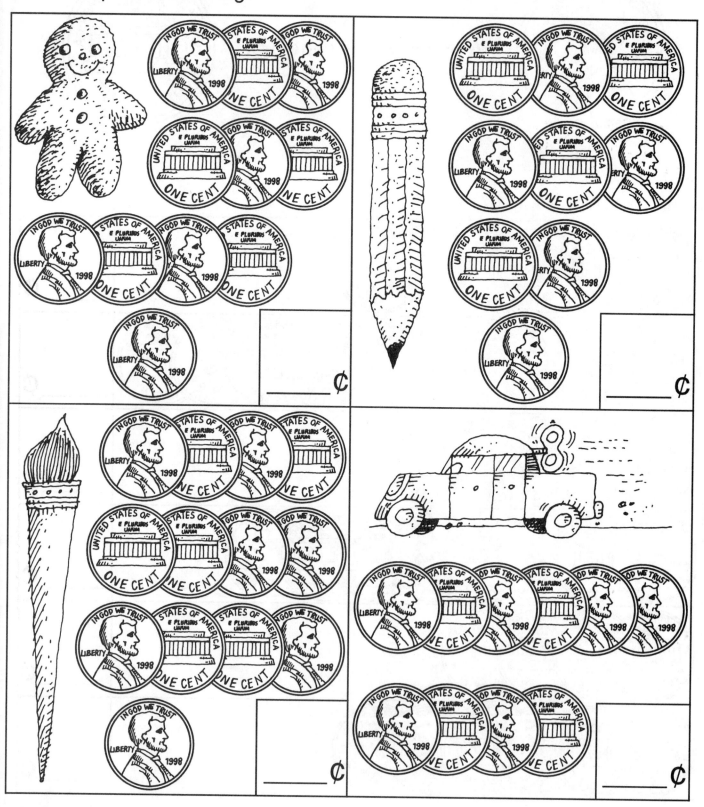

_____ ¢

_____ ¢

_____ ¢

_____ ¢

Skills: Counting and writing money values

MATH

A nickel = five cents (5¢).

1 = 5

How many nickels?
Now count by 5s. How many cents?

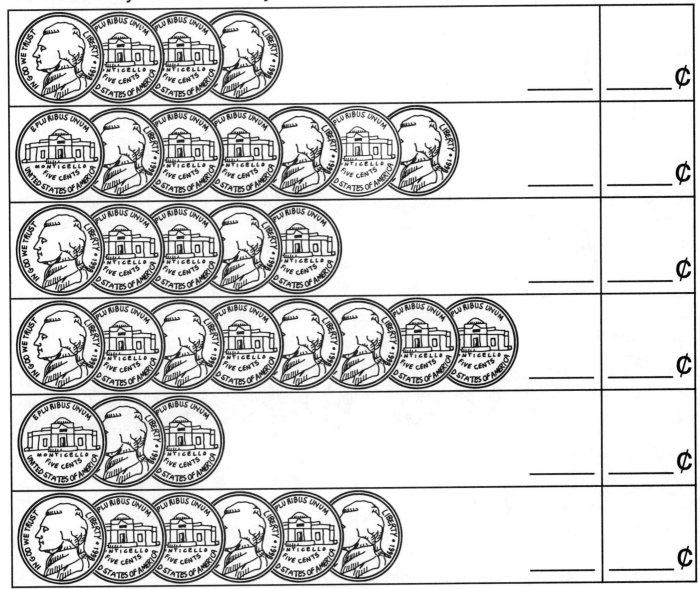

Skills: Counting; Writing money values

MATH

A dime = ten cents (10¢).

 1 ... = 10 ... 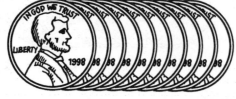 1 ... = 2 ...

Jan's class collected money for the needy.
Here's what Jan collected each day.
How many cents in each box?

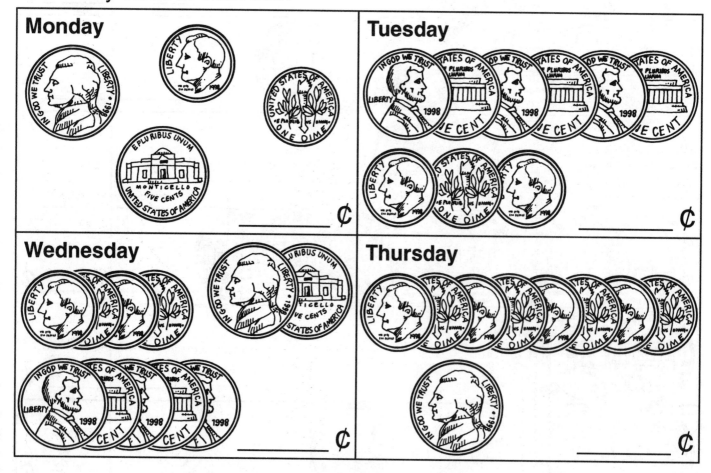

Monday	Tuesday
_____ ¢	_____ ¢
Wednesday	**Thursday**
_____ ¢	_____ ¢

Now add the sums. How much did Jan collect in all? _____

Skills: Recognizing money denominations; Adding

MATH

= 25 pennies

= 5 nickels

A quarter = 25 cents.

= 2 dimes and 1 nickel

How many quarters can you find in the picture below? _____

How many dimes? _____   How many nickels? _____

How many pennies? _____   How many coins in all? _____

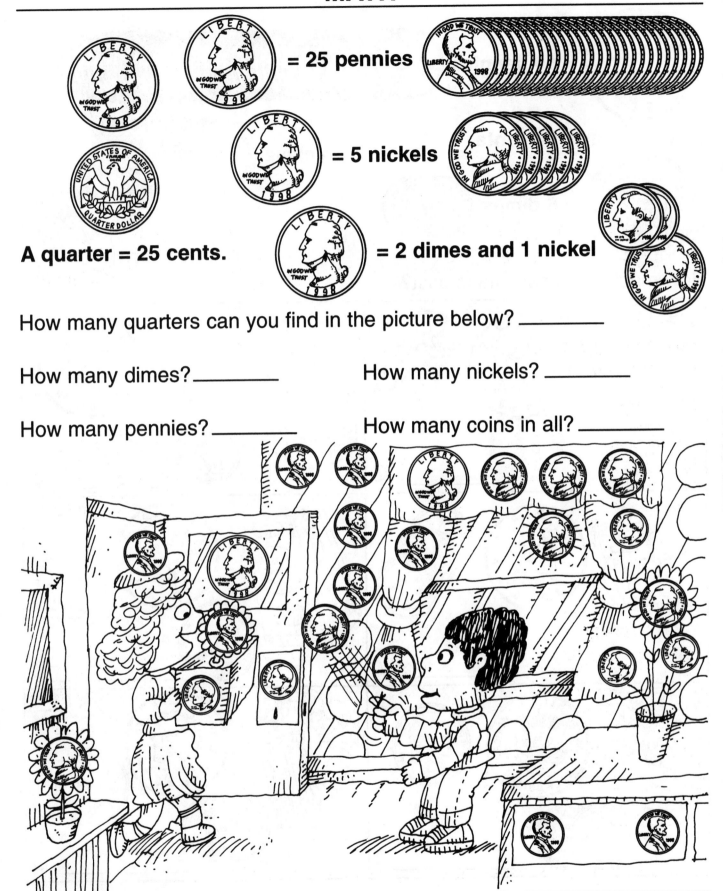

Skills: Recognizing money denominations; Counting

MATH

 = 50 pennies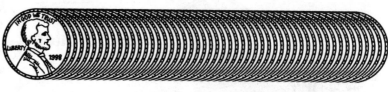

A half dollar = 50 cents.

 = 10 nickels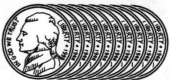

= 5 dimes

= 2 quarters

How much does each thing cost?

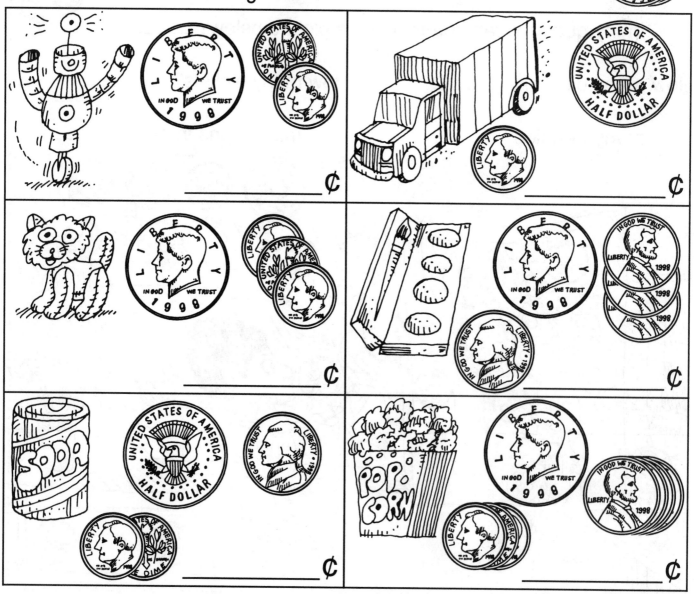

_____ ¢

_____ ¢

_____ ¢

_____ ¢

_____ ¢

_____ ¢

Skills: Recognizing money denominations; Adding

MATH

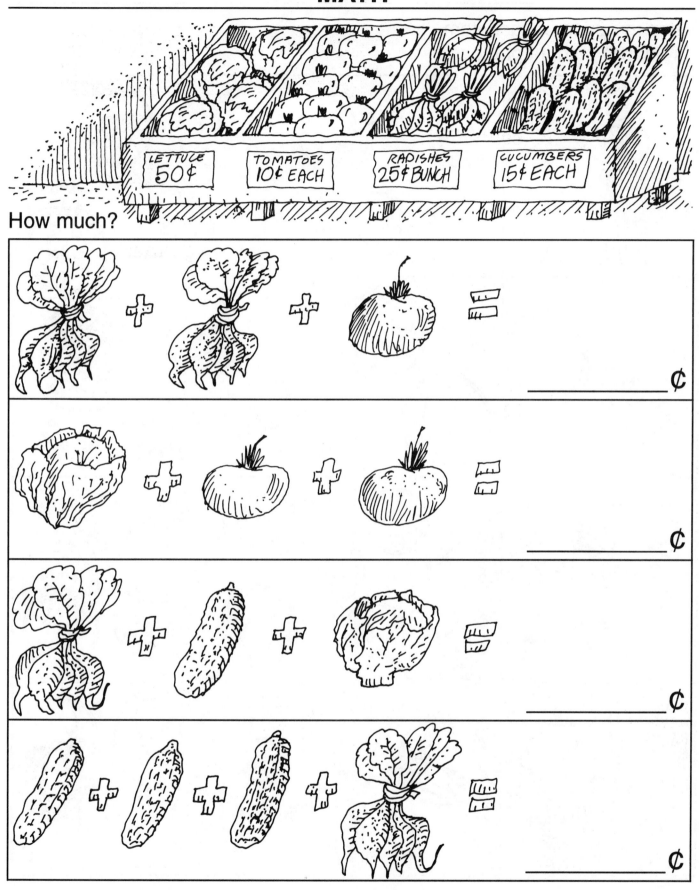

How much?

_____ ¢

_____ ¢

_____ ¢

_____ ¢

Skills: Money; Matching; Adding

MATH

Read the price of each item.
Circle that amount of money.

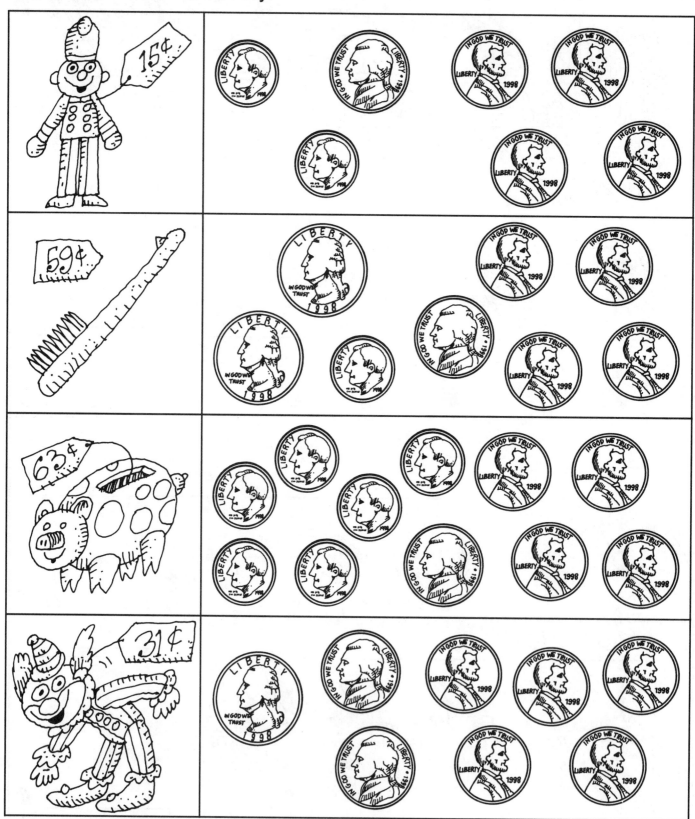

Skills: Understanding money values

MATH

Look at each price. Look at what someone paid.
How much change should the person get? (Hint: subtract)

Skills: Making change

MATH

A one-dollar bill  = $1.00

 = 4 quarters

 = 20 nickels

 = 10 dimes

= 100 pennies

Look at these bills.
Draw a line between the matching bills.

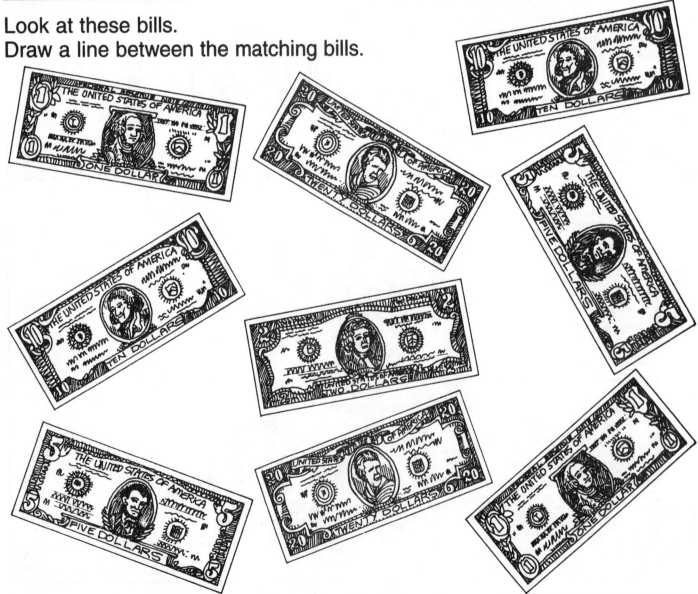

Skills: Understanding money value; Visual discrimination

MATH

Look at each price. Look at what someone paid.
How much change should the person get?

99¢   THE UNITED STATES OF AMERICA   ONE DOLLAR   _____ ¢

75¢   THE UNITED STATES OF AMERICA   ONE DOLLAR   _____ ¢

56¢   THE UNITED STATES OF AMERICA   ONE DOLLAR   _____ ¢

79¢   THE UNITED STATES OF AMERICA   ONE DOLLAR   _____ ¢

Skills: Making change; Subtracting

MATH

"What kind of ice cream do you like?" Mr. Curry asked his class.

"I like chocolate best," said Jerry.

"I like strawberry," added Anna.

"I like bubblegum," said Sabrina.

"Wait," said Mr. Curry, "I want to write these flavors on the board so we can vote for our four favorite flavors." Mr. Curry read each flavor. Kids who liked it raised their hands. Mr. Curry counted, or tallied, the votes. He helped the kids make a graph to show the voting results.

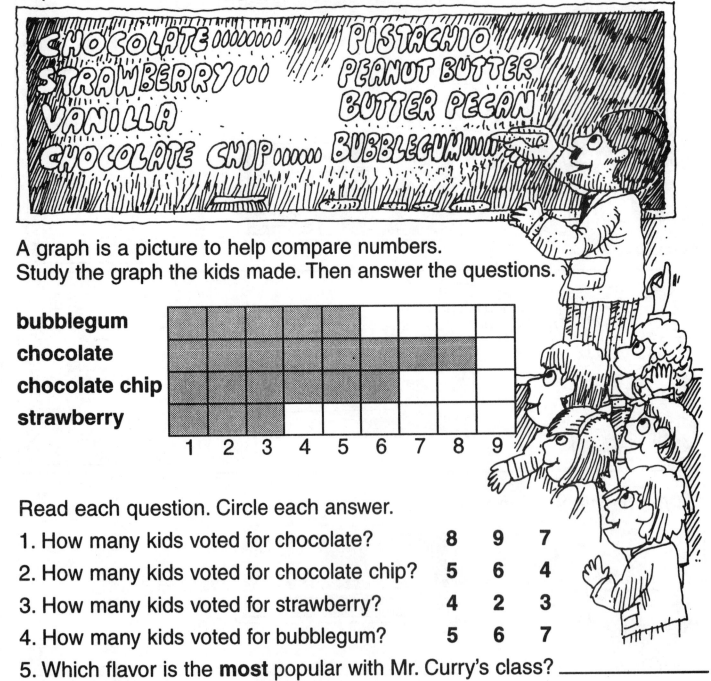

A graph is a picture to help compare numbers.
Study the graph the kids made. Then answer the questions.

Read each question. Circle each answer.

1. How many kids voted for chocolate?   **8**   **9**   **7**

2. How many kids voted for chocolate chip?   **5**   **6**   **4**

3. How many kids voted for strawberry?   **4**   **2**   **3**

4. How many kids voted for bubblegum?   **5**   **6**   **7**

5. Which flavor is the **most** popular with Mr. Curry's class? _____

Skills: Reading and interpreting graphs

MATH

Alan and his friends like to play video games. The kids keep score to see who wins the most games. Each star means a win.
Study their **picture graph**, then answer the questions.

Alan	☆ ☆ ☆ ☆
Sabrina	☆ ☆ ☆ ☆ ☆ ☆
Eric	☆ ☆ ☆ ☆ ☆
Nicole	☆ ☆ ☆
Bobby	☆ ☆

1. How many games has Nicole won? _____

2. How many games has Alan won? _____

3. Who has won the most games? _____

4. Who has won the fewest games? _____

5. Did Nicole win more games than Eric? **Yes**   **No**

6. Did Sabrina win 2 games more than Alan? **Yes**   **No**

7. Who won 3 games more than Nicole? _____

Skills: Reading and interpreting graphs

MATH

Some second graders read lots of books during the summer. Mrs. Cruz, the librarian, keeps a **picture graph**. It shows how many books each kid has read.

Paula	
Rosita	
Jenny	
Peter	
Luis	

1. How many books did Jenny read? _____

2. How many books did Paula read? _____

3. Who read the most books? _____

4. Who read the fewest books? _____

5. Did Jenny read more books than Rosita?   **Yes**   **No**

6. Did Peter read 3 books more than Jenny?   **Yes**   **No**

7. Who read 3 books fewer than Luis? _____

Skills: Reading and interpreting graphs

MATH

Shapes are everywhere.

Find squares. ☐

Find triangles. △

Find circles. ○

Find rectangles. ▭

How many squares? _____

How many triangles? _____

How many circles? _____

How many rectangles? _____

Skills: Recognizing and counting basic geometric shapes

MATH

Draw 2 things shaped like circles.

Draw 2 things shaped like squares.

Draw 2 things shaped like rectangles.

Draw 2 things shaped like triangles.

Skills: Recognizing and drawing basic geometric shapes

MATH

Color the one that is the same shape and size.

Skills: Matching basic geometric shapes

MATH

Copy each shape. Write how many sides it has.

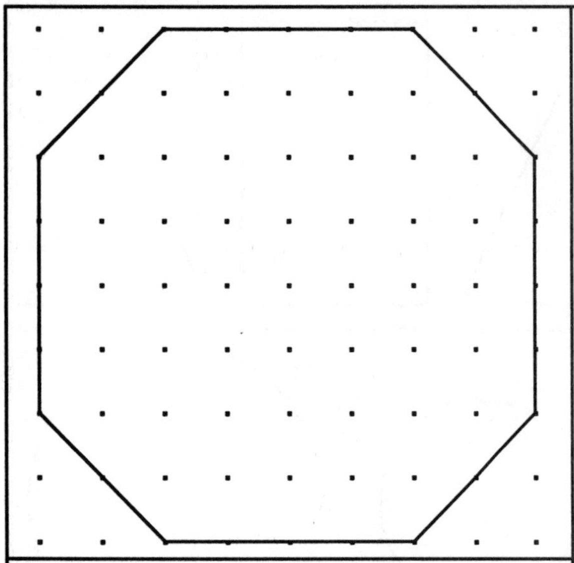

_____ sides

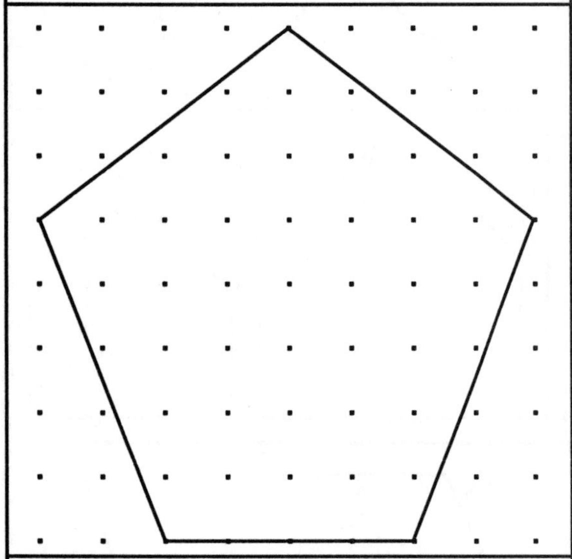

_____ sides

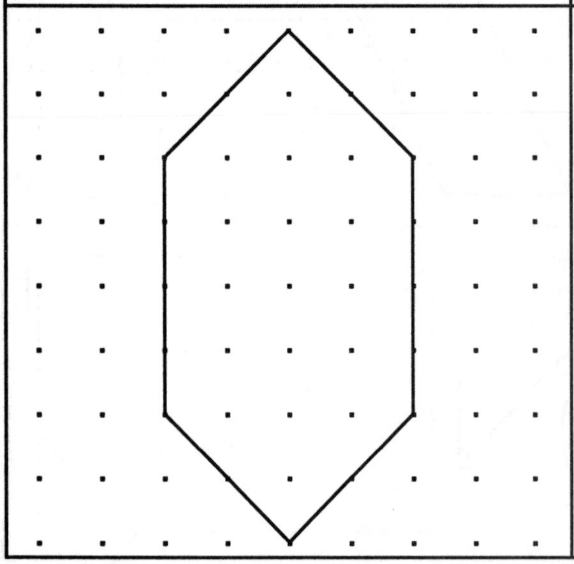

_____ sides

Skills: Drawing geometric shapes

MATH

Color the shape the solid looks most like.

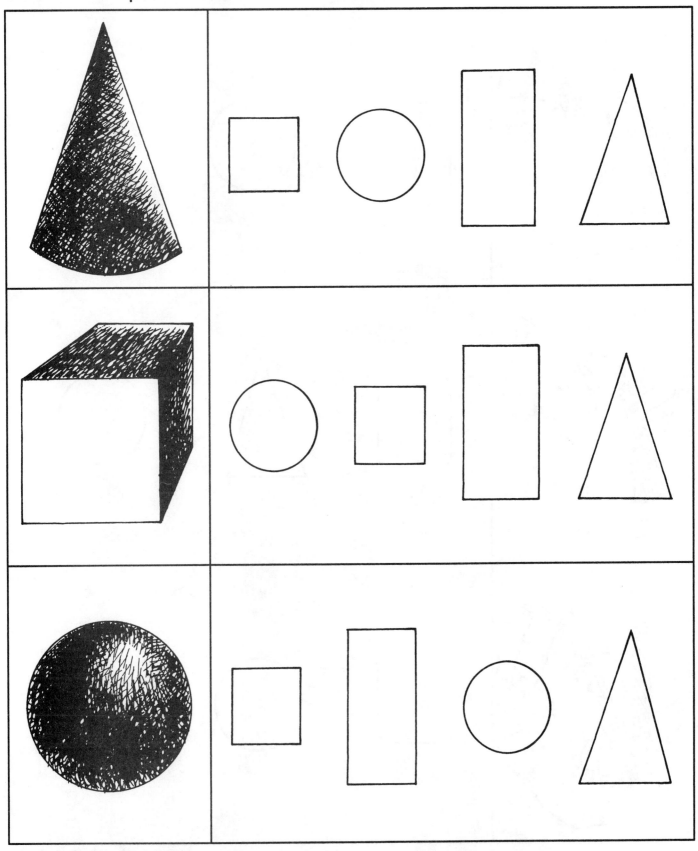

Skills: Matching geometric shapes to solids

MATH

Which would you get if you traced the solid?

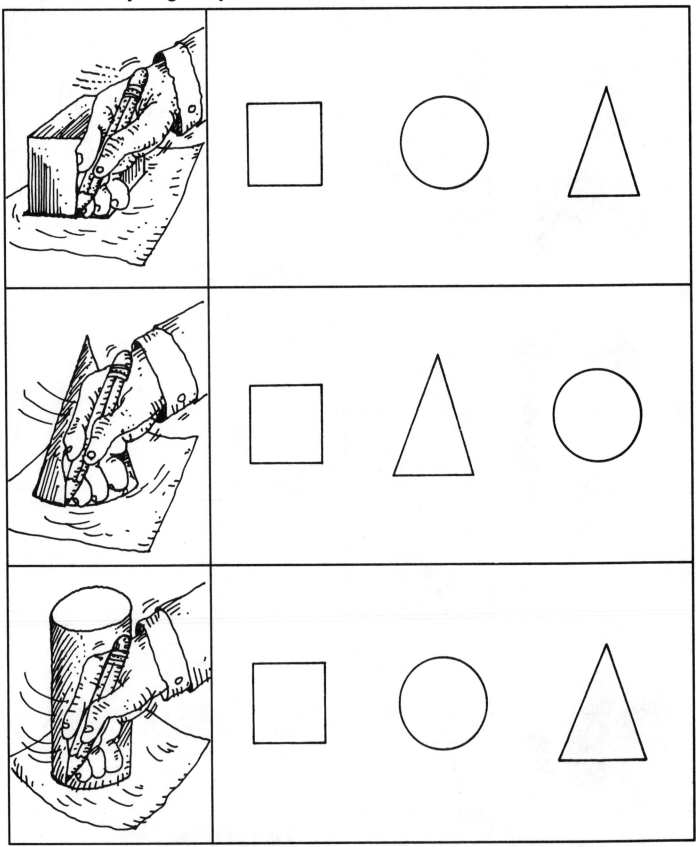

Skills: Discovering relationships between shapes and solids

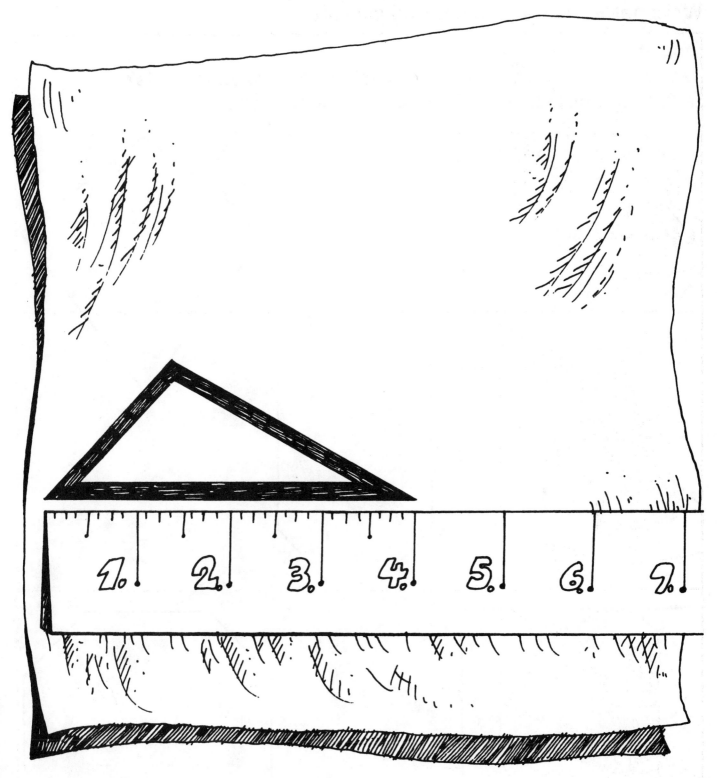

- Use a ruler.
- Measure each side of this triangle.
- Add those three numbers together.
- The sum is the length or perimeter around the whole triangle!

Skills: Calculating the perimeter of plane shapes

MATH

Equal parts

Look at each shape.
Can you draw one line in each shape to make two equal parts?
Each part is called a half. Color one half of each shape.

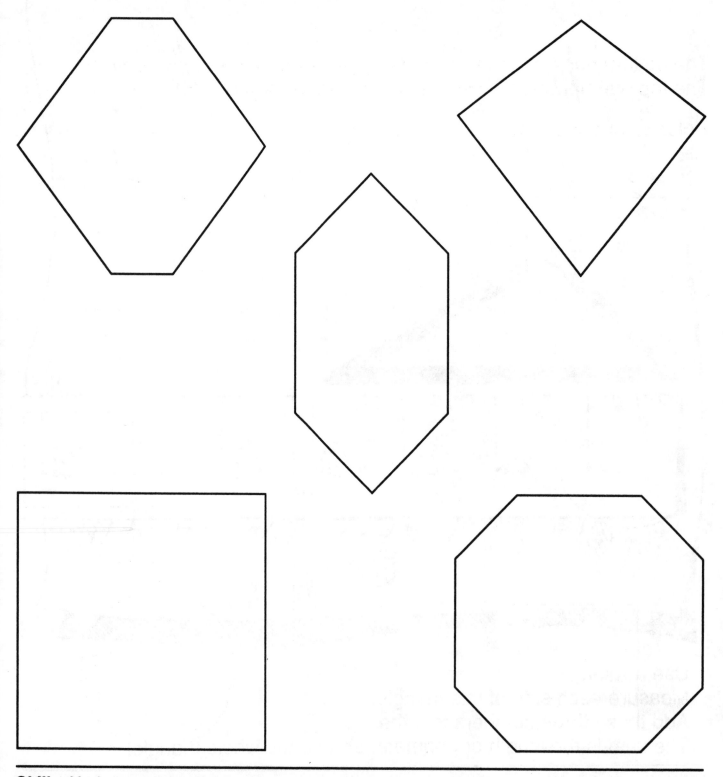

Skills: Understanding and showing two equal parts or one half

Half

This shape has 2 equal parts.
Each part is called a half.
Fractions are written as numbers above and below a line.

One half = $\frac{1}{2}$.

The bottom number shows how many parts the whole is divided into.
The top number shows how many of those parts you have.

Color $\frac{1}{2}$ of each shape.

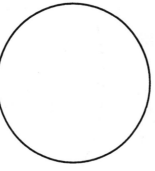
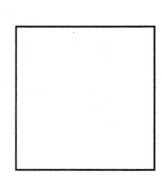

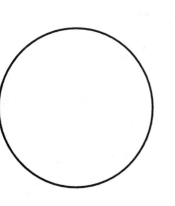

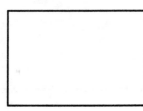

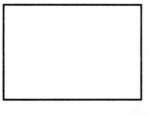
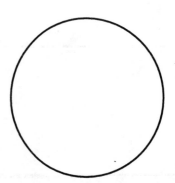

Skills: Recognizing halves; Recognizing fractions

MATH

Thirds

This shape has 3 equal parts, or **thirds**.

Each part equals $\frac{1}{3}$.

Color $\frac{1}{3}$ of the circle.

Color $\frac{2}{3}$ of the square.

Skills: Recognizing fractions; Showing thirds

MATH

Fourths

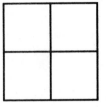

This shape has 4 equal parts, or **fourths**.

Each part is equal to $\frac{1}{4}$.

- Color $\frac{1}{4}$ of the pizza.

- Color $\frac{2}{4}$ of the sandwich.

- Color $\frac{3}{4}$ of the cake.

What do you notice about the $\frac{2}{4}$?

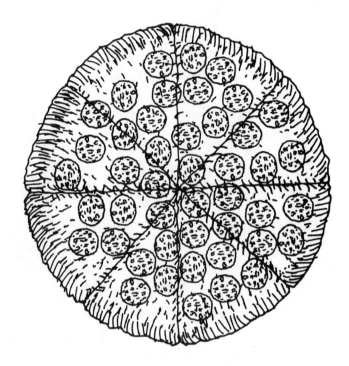

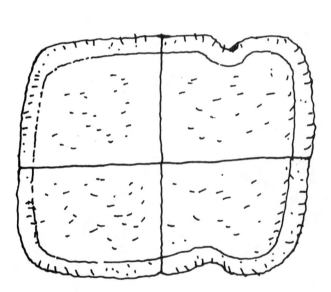

Skills: Recognizing fractions and showing fourths

PRACTICE PAGE

GRAMMAR

A **sentence** tells a complete idea.

| Pandas are animals. | This is a sentence.

The sentence is about pandas.
It tells a complete idea about pandas.

| Pandas | This is **not** a sentence.

The word doesn't tell a complete idea.

Circle each **sentence** below.

Pandas are black and white.

The animals

Pandas eat bamboo shoots.

In the zoo

Is the bamboo yummy?

Now the pandas

Did you know pandas come from China?

Skills: Identifying sentences

GRAMMAR

All sentences begin with a capital letter.

- A **statement** is a sentence that tells something. A statement ends with a period (**.**).

- A **question** is a sentence that asks something. A question ends with a question mark (**?**).

Write **S** in front of each **statement**. Write **Q** in front of each **question**.

_____ "We went to the carnival last week."

_____ "Did you eat cotton candy?"

_____ "Yes, and I got a red balloon."

_____ "I wish I had a blue balloon."

_____ "Did your little brother go on the merry-go-round?"

_____ "No, he was too scared to go."

_____ "Was the carnival fun?"

_____ "Yes, I wish you could have been there."

_____ "Maybe I can go next time the carnival comes to town."

Skills: Identifying statements and questions

GRAMMAR

Read each sentence. If it is a **statement**, re-write it as a **question**.
If it is a **question**, make it a **statement**.
The first one has been done for you.

Is it Rosita's birthday?
It is Rosita's birthday.

There are many people at the party.

_____

Will Rosita break the piñata?

_____

This party is fun.

_____

The cake will be yummy.

_____

Rosita is my best friend.

_____

Will you come to my party next week?

_____

Skills: Identifying and writing statements and questions

GRAMMAR

Look at the picture. Think about what's happening.
Then write two **statements** and two **questions** to go with the picture-story.
Use words from the word bag to help you.

park fly play fun
dog kites baby ride
bike birds sky day
mother cry lost

Statement: _____

Question: _____

Statement: _____

Question: _____

Skills: Writing statements and questions

GRAMMAR

All sentences begin with a capital letter.

- Some sentences show **surprise** or **strong feelings**.
  End these sentences with an exclamation mark (!).
  I got a bike for my birthday!

- Some sentences give orders or commands.
  End most of these sentences with a period (.).
  Put your clothes away.

- If the order is urgent, use an exclamation mark (!).
  Look out for that snake!

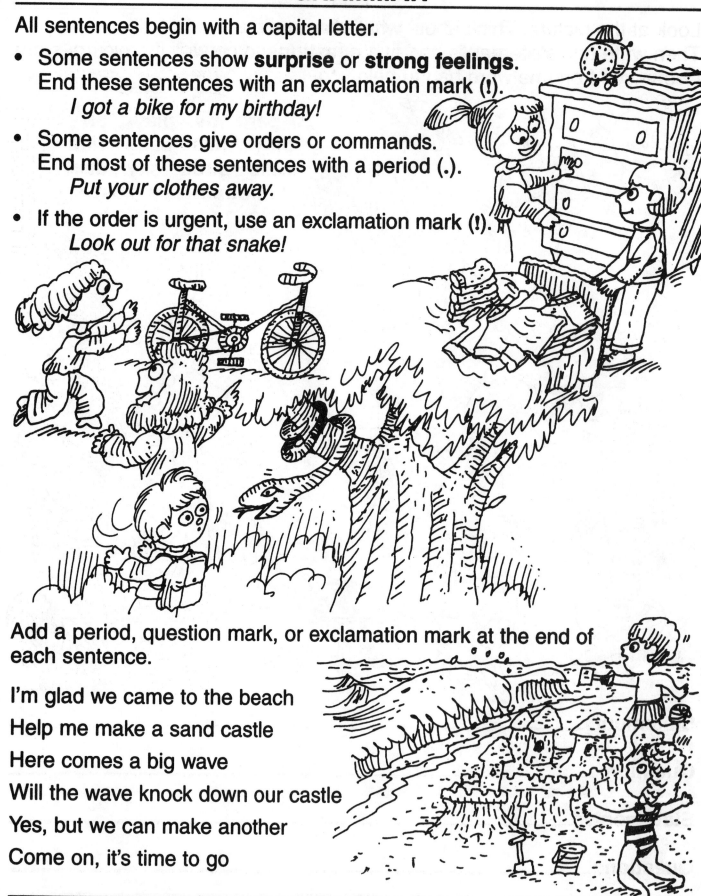

Add a period, question mark, or exclamation mark at the end of each sentence.

I'm glad we came to the beach

Help me make a sand castle

Here comes a big wave

Will the wave knock down our castle

Yes, but we can make another

Come on, it's time to go

Skills: Punctuation (exclamations, commands)

GRAMMAR

Look at the picture. Think about what's happening.
Then write one **statement**, one **question**, one **exclamation**, and one
command to go with the picture-story. The words in the word bag may
help you.

shop   family   ride   up
down   carry   packages
noise   music   people
boxes   escalators

Statement: _____

Question: _____

Exclamation: _____

Command: _____

Skills: Writing the four kinds of sentences

GRAMMAR

Every sentence has two parts.

- The **subject**, or *naming part*, tells who or what the sentence is about.
- The **predicate**, or *telling part*, tells what the subject does or did.

Draw a line from each subject to the right predicate.

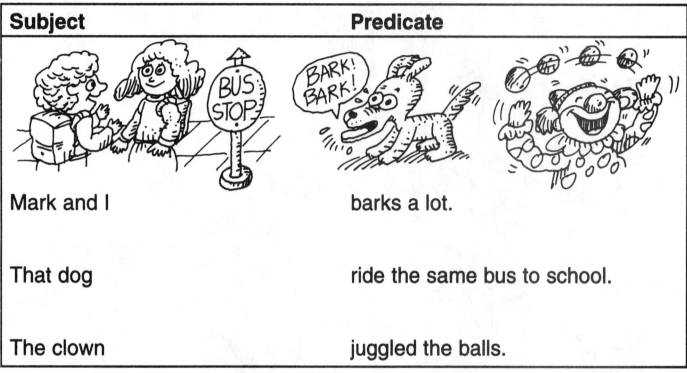

Subject	Predicate
Mark and I	barks a lot.
That dog	ride the same bus to school.
The clown	juggled the balls.

Now read each sentence. Circle the **subject**. Underline the **predicate**.

Our class went to the library.

Joey found a book about space.

The librarian stamps our books.

The library is a nice place.

I'm going to go back next week.

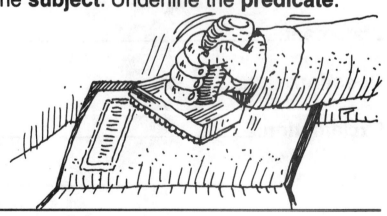

Skills: Identifying sentence parts

GRAMMAR

Read each sentence. Then write the **subject** on the line.

The baby is one year old. _____

My dad drives a bus. _____

Grandma baked a pie. _____

Our cat had kittens. _____

Read each sentence. Then write the **predicate** on the line.

Our teacher came to my house. _____

My family has a new car. _____

That chair is broken. _____

Books are fun to read. _____

Draw lines to match the sentence parts.

Subject

Trees

My shoes

A groundhog

The weather

Predicate

hurt my feet.

lives underground.

has been very cold.

grow in a forest.

Skills: Identifying sentence parts

GRAMMAR

Remember that every sentence has a **subject** and a **predicate**.

| ground covers ice boy throw girl |
| hill skis man play sled snowballs |

Write the missing **subject** or **predicate**. Use the word box to help you.

The snow _____.

_____ is making a snowman.

The children _____.

_____ is slippery and steep!

The man _____.

Skills: Understanding and writing sentence parts

146

GRAMMAR

You can join two sentences that tell related ideas.

- Use **and** to join sentences with similar ideas.

    Cats have kittens. Dogs have puppies.
    Cats have kittens **and** dogs have puppies.

- Use **but** to join sentences with contrasting ideas.

    Mom likes chocolate. Dad doesn't.
    Mom likes chocolate **but** dad doesn't.

Read the sentences. Join them using **and** or **but**.

Katie likes ladybugs. So does her sister.

_____

_____

My favorite class is gym. My sister likes art better.

_____

_____

_____

Skills: Writing compound sentences

GRAMMAR

- Use **or** to join sentences that show different possibilities.

    We could bake a cake. We could buy a cake.
    We could bake a cake **or** we could buy a cake.

- Use **because** to join sentences that tell what and why.

    I am happy. Our team won.
    I am happy **because** our team won.

Read the sentences. Join them using **or** or **because**.

Max is sad. His dog is lost.

_____

We can go to the zoo. We can play in the park.

_____

_____

Skills: Writing compound sentences

GRAMMAR

A **noun** names a person, place, or thing.

A **common noun** names any person, place, or thing.

| baby | school | soda | day |

A **proper noun** names a specific person, place, or thing.
Begin a proper noun with a capital letter.

| Brandon | Barnes School | Fizzy Soda | Monday |

Read each sentence. Circle each **noun**.

Here comes Chris.

We will ride to the park.

We will meet our friends in Cresky Park.

We ride our bikes every Saturday.

Do you have a bike, too?

Skills: Identifying nouns

GRAMMAR

Remember that **proper nouns** tell about specific people, places, and things. And proper nouns always start with a capital letter.

Read each sentence. Circle each **proper noun**.

We went to New York City on vacation.

Dad took me to a show at Radio City Music Hall.

We saw my cousin Lin Yu in a play on Broadway.

On Saturday, Dad and I went to the Bronx Zoo.

On Sunday, we took a walk in Central Park.

Then we flew home to Springfield.

Skills: Identifying proper nouns

GRAMMAR

Add **–s** to most nouns to mean more than one.

car   cars

Add **–s** to make the word that means **more than one**.

flower   _____

hat   _____

book   _____

bowl   _____

Skills: Understanding plurals with –s endings

GRAMMAR

Nouns that end in certain sounds add **–es** to mean more than one.

bus	**buses**
kiss	**kisses**
fox	**foxes**
patch	**patches**

Add the necessary letters.

inch___

watch___

box___

witch___

Skills: Forming plural nouns

GRAMMAR

Some special words don't add **-s** to mean more than one.
Here are some you often see.

1 man	2 men
1 woman	3 women
1 child	2 children
1 tooth	8 teeth
1 foot	2 feet
1 mouse	3 mice

Match each noun to the right picture.

tooth

teeth

man

men

foot

feet

Skills: Identifying irregular plurals

GRAMMAR

Sometimes two words can be joined to make one word.
The new word is called a **compound word**.

tooth + brush = toothbrush

Write the two words that make each compound word.

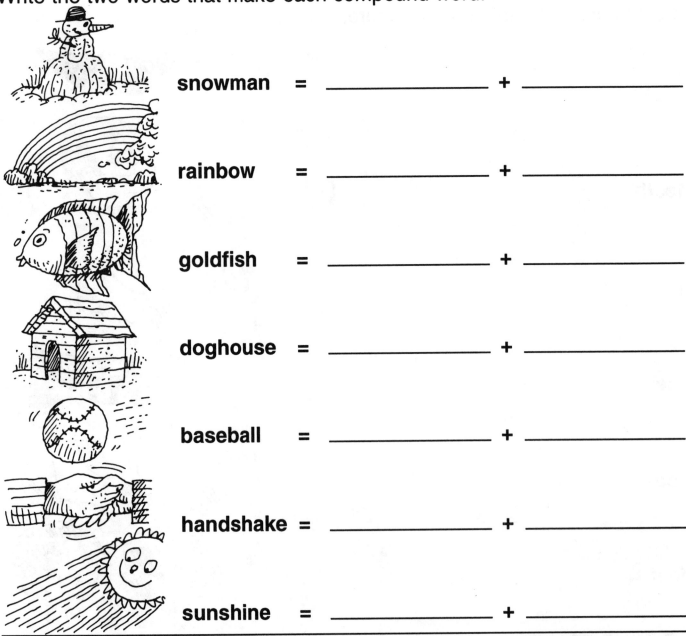

snowman = _____ + _____

rainbow = _____ + _____

goldfish = _____ + _____

doghouse = _____ + _____

baseball = _____ + _____

handshake = _____ + _____

sunshine = _____ + _____

Skills: Identifying compound words

GRAMMAR

Draw a line between the two words that make a compound word.

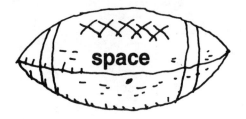 space

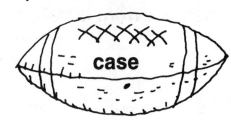 case

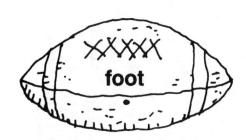 foot

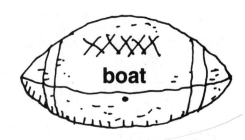 boat

 news

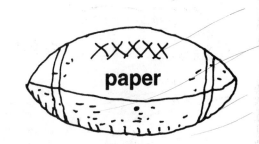 paper

 sail

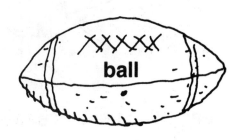 ball

 book

 ship

Skills: Identifying compound words

GRAMMAR

A **verb** is an action word. It tells what is happening.
Without verbs, nothing would ever happen!

> Sam and I **walk** to school.

The word **walk** is a verb. It tells what Sam and I are doing.

Read each sentence. Circle each **verb** that tells what's happening.

Some kids ride a bus.

Pam's mother drives her to school.

We meet outside.

We go to our classroom.

At lunch time, we eat lunch together.

Skills: Identifying verbs

GRAMMAR

Verbs change depending on who is doing them.
Verbs that tell about one person or thing usually end in **–s**.

> Pete reads. Pete smiles. Pete eats.

To tell about yourself, the person you are talking to, or more than one person, leave off the **–s**.

Circle the correct **verb**.

Mother **grow / grows** flowers in her garden.

Rick and Mother **work / works** in the garden.

Rick **pick / picks** some pretty flowers.

We all **eat / eats** tomatoes for dinner!

Do you **like / likes** to grow things, too?

Skills: Understanding subject–verb agreement

GRAMMAR

Verbs can tell about actions that are happening now, in the **present**.
Add **–ed** to verbs to tell about what already happened in the **past**.
(If the verb already ends in **e**, just add **–d**.)

> Today we skate.
> Yesterday we skat**ed**.

Read the verbs below. **Circle** the ones that tell about the **present**.
Underline the ones that tell about the **past**.

visit	happened	drop
walked	skip	cooked
shout	bounced	toss
stopped	quack	hiked
plant	sew	washed
asked	listen	talk
color	marched	tiptoe
baked	pull	poked
bother	look	counted
paint	jumped	learned
glided	splash	turned

Skills: Identifying verbs in present and past tenses

GRAMMAR

The verb **be** is a special verb. It doesn't follow the rules.
So **be** is an **irregular verb**.

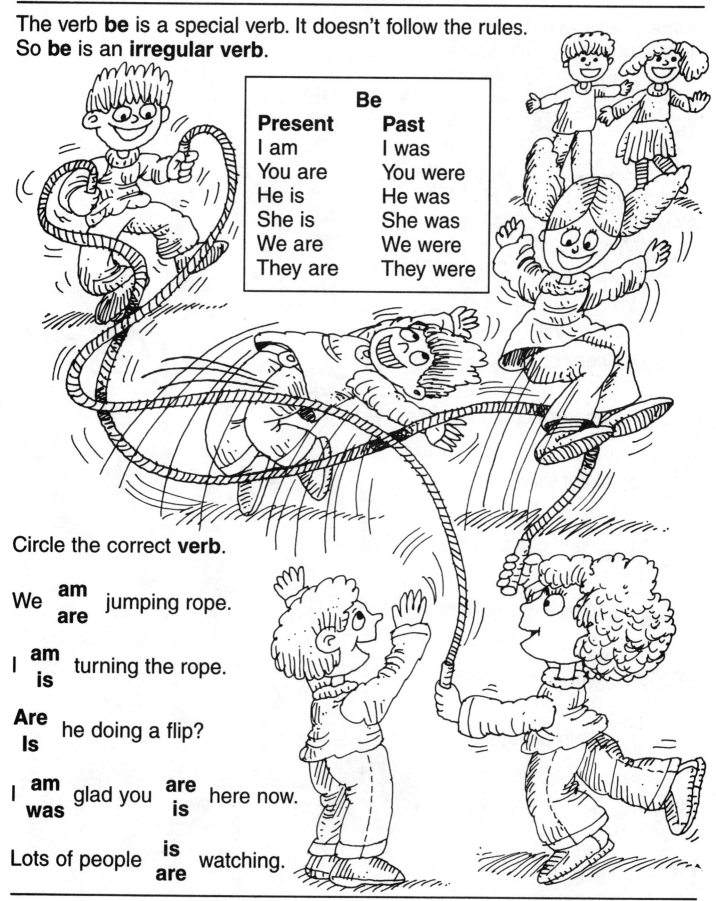

	Be	
Present	**Past**	
I am	I was	
You are	You were	
He is	He was	
She is	She was	
We are	We were	
They are	They were	

Circle the correct **verb**.

We **am** / **are** jumping rope.

I **am** / **is** turning the rope.

Are / **Is** he doing a flip?

I **am** / **was** glad you **are** / **is** here now.

Lots of people **is** / **are** watching.

Skills: Using the irregular verb be

159

GRAMMAR

Some special verbs don't add **–ed** to tell about the past.
Here are some you often use.

Present	Past
am	was
are	were
give	gave
take	took
do	did
go	went
come	came
run	ran

Circle the correct **verb**.

I **go** / **went** to another camp last year.

Do / **Did** you like it there?

No, I **like** / **liked** this camp better.

I **am** / **was** glad you are here now.

Do you **want** / **wanted** a hot dog?

No, I **eat** / **ate** a big breakfast.

Well, I **am** / **was** hungry now!

Please **give** / **gave** me a hot dog!

Skills: Using present and past verb tenses

GRAMMAR

The verb **have** is an **irregular verb** because it does not follow the **–ed** rule.

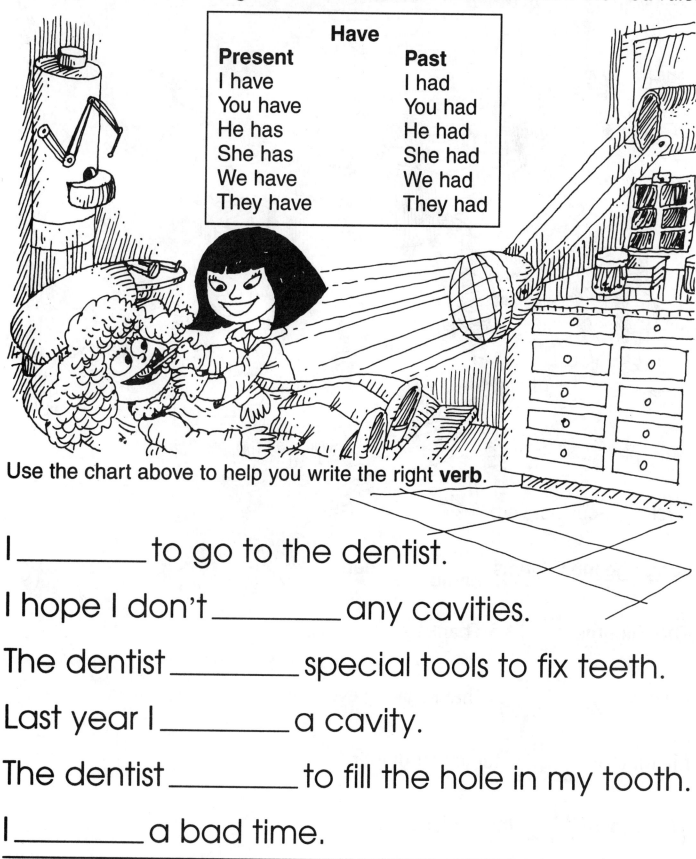

Have	
Present	**Past**
I have	I had
You have	You had
He has	He had
She has	She had
We have	We had
They have	They had

Use the chart above to help you write the right **verb**.

I _____ to go to the dentist.

I hope I don't _____ any cavities.

The dentist _____ special tools to fix teeth.

Last year I _____ a cavity.

The dentist _____ to fill the hole in my tooth.

I _____ a bad time.

Skills: Using the irregular verb have

Circle the correct verb.

Long ago the Pilgrims **come** / **came** to America.

The Pilgrims **have** / **had** a Thanksgiving party.

Now we **celebrate** / **celebrated** Thanksgiving every year.

My Mother **cook** / **cooks** turkey for dinner.

We always **give** / **gave** thanks for our food.

Skills: Using past and present verb forms; Social studies

GRAMMAR

Here are some more special **verbs**.

Present	Past
grow/grows	grew
eat/eats	ate
know/knows	knew
see/sees	saw
write/writes	wrote

Write the correct **verb**.

"I like to _____ apples."

"I had a pear, but my brother _____ it."

"When you plant an apple seed, it _____ into a tree."

"I once _____ a bean pod from a seed."

"Can you _____ the mountains from here?"

"No, but I once _____ a mountain in Switzerland."

"Do you _____ Sam?"

"No, but my father _____ his father."

Skills: Using present and past verb tenses

163

GRAMMAR

The words **he**, **she**, **it**, and **they** are **pronouns**. These words take the place of a noun. The pronoun **you** replaces the name of the person to whom you are speaking.

Alan	**Sabrina**	**wagon**
he	she	it

Alan and Sabrina
they

Write **pronouns** in the story for the words in **( )**.

_____ had a wagon. _____ had some
(Alan)   (Sabrina)

pumpkins. _____ put the pumpkins in
          (Alan and Sabrina)

the wagon. ___ bumped down the street.
           (The wagon)

   Alan saw his neighbor. "Do _____ want to
                              (a neighbor)

buy a pumpkin?" asked Alan. The neighbor

did buy two pumpkins. But _____ still had a lot
                         (Alan and Sabrina)

of pumpkins.

   So _____ took the pumpkins back home.
      (Alan and Sabrina)

And their mother baked some pumpkin pies.

_____ is a very good cook!
(Mother)

Skills: Writing pronouns

GRAMMAR

I and **me** are **pronouns** about you. Use **I** as the subject of a sentence. Use **me** after a **verb** or a **preposition** (for, with, about, etc.). And always name yourself last when you talk about yourself and other people.

Circle the correct **pronoun.**

Bobby, Eric, and $\begin{smallmatrix}I\\me\end{smallmatrix}$ like to hike.

Mom made snacks for my friends and $\begin{smallmatrix}I\\me\end{smallmatrix}$ to take along.

" $\begin{smallmatrix}I\\me\end{smallmatrix}$ want to go, too," said my little sister.

"She's not coming, is she?" Bobby asked $\begin{smallmatrix}I\\me\end{smallmatrix}$

"No," $\begin{smallmatrix}I\\me\end{smallmatrix}$ said. "She's too little."

$\begin{smallmatrix}I\\me\end{smallmatrix}$ looked at my sister.

"Later you can play a game with my friends and $\begin{smallmatrix}I\\me\end{smallmatrix}$," $\begin{smallmatrix}I\\me\end{smallmatrix}$ told her.

She smiled, then $\begin{smallmatrix}I\\me\end{smallmatrix}$ waved good-bye.

My friends and $\begin{smallmatrix}I\\me\end{smallmatrix}$ went hiking!

Skills: Using the pronouns **I** and **me**

GRAMMAR

To show ownership, add **–'s** to a noun.

> Pete has some money. It is Pete's money.

Fill in the missing words below.

Kathy has a cat.

It is _____ cat.

Joe has a bike.

It is _____ bike.

Mom has two hats.

They are _____ hats.

Skills: Possessive form of nouns

GRAMMAR

Remember to use an **apostrophe** (') to show that something belongs to someone. If the thing belongs to one person, use –**'s**. If it belongs to more than one person, use –**s'**.

> This is a girl**'s** coat.
> Where are the boy**s'** coats?

Write the possessive that means the same as the words in parentheses.

Those are (belonging to Sam) gloves. _____

Are these (belonging to some girls) coats? _____

Who left this (belonging to a boy) hat? _____

What is that in (belonging to Dad) hand? _____

I think it's (belonging to Jana) coat. _____

Are we going home in your (belonging to mom) car? _____

Skills: Using possessives; Spelling

GRAMMAR

Read each clue. Write the answer in the crossword puzzle.
Be sure to write the apostrophe with the letter **-s**.

Down

1. Belonging to one girl
2. Belonging to everyone (**Hint**: Don't be tricked.
   Check the last three letters on the word!)
3. Belonging to Robbie
7. Belonging to hearts

Across

4. Belonging to a boy
5. Belonging to a baby
6. Belonging to some elephants
8. Belonging to Al
9. Belonging to lots of dogs

Skills: Using possessives

GRAMMAR

Pronouns can also be used to show who owns or **possesses** something. Here are some **possessive pronouns** we often use:

my	mine	your	yours	his
her	hers	our	ours	their	his
					theirs

Circle the correct **pronouns** in the story.

We / Our school had a carnival. Lots of kids came with **they / their** parents.

"Are you going to get **you / your** face painted?" asked **mine / my** friend Courtney.

"Yes," I said, "I want it just like **your / yours** !"

Dad bought a plant for **him / his** office. Mom sold lots of **she / her** cookies.

Courtney and I bought some of **her / hers** when we got hungry. **Our / We** made

lots of money to help the school.

Skills: Using possessive pronouns

GRAMMAR

A and **an** are **articles**. They may be small, but they are important.
You use them with nouns when you don't mean a specific person or thing.
Remember: use **a** if a word starts with a consonant.
Use **an** if a word starts with a vowel.

> **an airplane   a tiger**

The is a definite article. It refers to a particular person or thing.
Write **a** or **an** in each sentence. Circle each **the**.

There is ____ banana on the table.

I think I'll have ____ apple.

Roger drank ____ glass of milk.

Is there ____ orange in the basket?

No, but I have ____ can of orange soda.

Skills: Using articles

GRAMMAR

An **adjective** describes, or tells more about, a noun or pronoun. Adjectives help paint pictures in your mind.

> I have a boat.
> I have a **blue** boat.

The word **blue** tells more about the noun **boat**. Can you see the blue boat in your mind?

Circle the **adjective** or **adjectives**.
Underline the **noun** or **pronoun** it describes.

Helen has a yellow boat.

It has big white sails.

My boat has striped sails.

It is a nice warm day.

I see lots of fluffy clouds.

Later I'll fly my new kite.

It is green.

Skills: Recognizing adjectives

GRAMMAR

Circle each **adjective**.
Hint: Remember, an adjective describes something.

funny	come	soft	sandy	sweet
red	hard	cloud	book	candy
sad	warm	cold	green	pencil
bear	happy	coat	loud	tree
pink	fish	tall	furry	angry

Write an **adjective** from the box to complete each sentence.
Underline the **noun** or **pronoun** it describes.

My puppy has a _____ coat.

Please turn down that _____ music!

A giraffe is very _____.

I like to play on a _____ beach.

I stepped on a _____ rock!

Look at the _____ clown!

That bear does not look _____.

Ice is _____.

Sunshine makes me feel _____.

The tree is _____.

Skills: Choosing appropriate adjectives

GRAMMAR

Adjectives can describe how big something is, or what color, or whether it's pretty. They can also tell how many.
Many, **some**, and **all** are some adjectives that tell how many.
Numbers can also be used as adjectives.

Circle the **adjective** that tells how many.

We saw some dolphins.

Every dolphin did tricks.

The trainer rode on one dolphin.

Then two dolphins leaped in the air.

The three dolphins even played basketball!

The dolphins had some fish as a reward.

There were 50 people at the show.

Many people stayed for the next show.

Skills: Identifying adjectives that tell how many

GRAMMAR

Color, **size**, and **shape** words are **adjectives** that tell what kind. Here are some you often use to describe things.

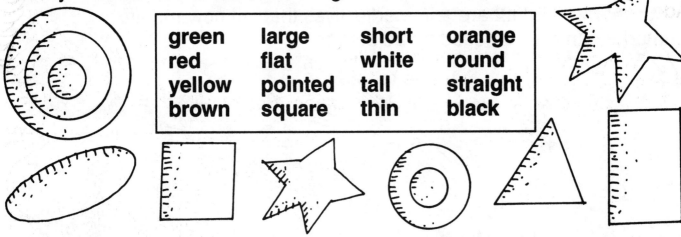

green	large	short	orange
red	flat	white	round
yellow	pointed	tall	straight
brown	square	thin	black

Look across and down to find these "what kind" adjectives hidden in the puzzle:

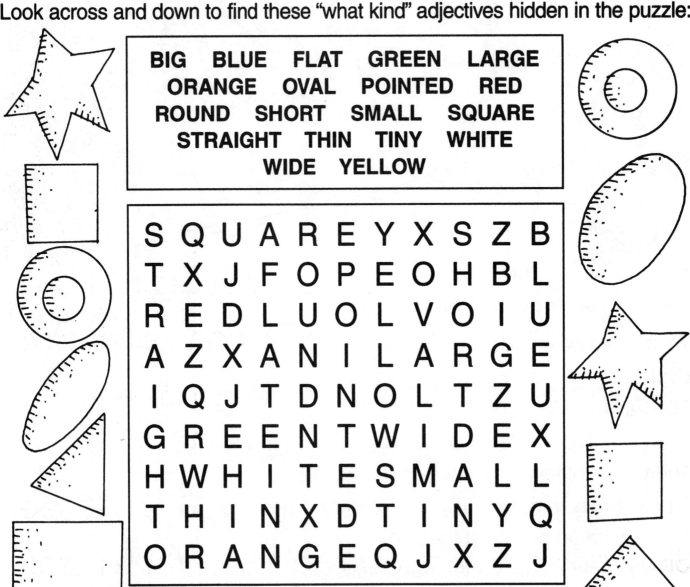

BIG BLUE FLAT GREEN LARGE
ORANGE OVAL POINTED RED
ROUND SHORT SMALL SQUARE
STRAIGHT THIN TINY WHITE
WIDE YELLOW

S Q U A R E Y X S Z B
T X J F O P E O H B L
R E D L U O L V O I U
A Z X A N I L A R G E
I Q J T D N O L T Z U
G R E E N T W I D E X
H W H I T E S M A L L
T H I N X D T I N Y Q
O R A N G E Q J X Z J

Skills: Identifying adjectives that describe color, size, and shape

GRAMMAR

You can use **adjectives** to compare nouns.
Add **–er** to compare two people, places, or things.
Add **–est** to compare more than two.

This tree is **tall**.
That tree is **taller**.
But here is the **tallest** tree of all!

Write **–er** or **–est** to make each adjective correct.

Gwen is tall___ than her sister.

Matt is the tall___ kid in our class.

I am young___ than Pam.

But I'm old___ than Matt.

Recess today was short___ than yesterday,

  because it's cold___ today than yesterday!

Last Friday was the cold___ day all year.

And the snow was deep___ than before.

I made the odd___ snowman you'll ever see.

Slow down, you're walking fast___ than I am!

Skills: Comparing with adjectives

GRAMMAR

Change the **y** at the end of an adjective to **i** before adding **–er** or **–est**.

That clown is **funny**.	My hands are **dirty**.
This one is **funnier**.	But yours are **dirtier**.
But here's the **funniest** of all.	And his are the **dirtiest** of all!

Do not add **–er** or **–est** to compare special adjectives.

This kind of juice is **good**.	That book report was **bad**.
That kind of juice is **better**.	But yours was even **worse**.
But this kind is the **best**!	And hers was the **worst** of all!

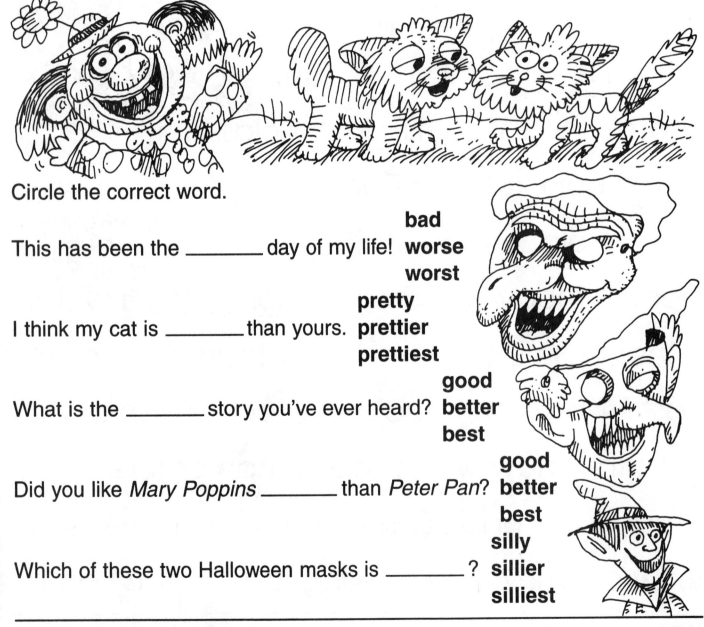

Circle the correct word.

This has been the _____ day of my life! **bad** **worse** **worst**

I think my cat is _____ than yours. **pretty** **prettier** **prettiest**

What is the _____ story you've ever heard? **good** **better** **best**

Did you like *Mary Poppins* _____ than *Peter Pan*? **good** **better** **best**

Which of these two Halloween masks is _____? **silly** **sillier** **silliest**

Skills: Comparing with adjectives

GRAMMAR

An **adverb** tells more about a verb. Adverbs can tell **when**, **where**, or **how** an action happens.

> **Today** we had a race.
> We like to run **outside**.
> We run **quickly**.

Today tells **when**. *Outside* tells **where**. *Quickly* tells **how**.

Circle the adverb. Write whether it tells **when**, **where**, or **how**.

I won a prize yesterday. _____

I ran speedily in the race. _____

I never thought I would win. _____

I marched proudly with other winners. _____

I stood up on a stage. _____

I looked around. _____

My friends smiled happily at me. _____

Skills: Identifying adverbs

GRAMMAR

Remember that **adverbs** tell **when**, **where**, or **how**.
Did you notice that many **how adverbs** end in **–ly**?

slowly	sweetly	cleverly	neatly
quickly	lately	loudly	softly
carelessly	happily	closely	angrily

Write a **how adverb** to complete each sentence.
Use the word box to help you.

I tried to paint _____.

But someone outside yelled _____.

I _____ splashed the paint!

My friend Jan _____ cleaned it up.

Jan had _____ hidden a mouse in her picture.

I looked _____, but I couldn't find it.

We painted _____ all afternoon.

Skills: Using adverbs

GRAMMAR

You can use **adverbs** to compare how things are done.
Add the word **more** to compare two ways.
Add the word **most** to compare more than two.

| carefully | more carefully | most carefully |
| helpfully | more helpfully | most helpfully |

Circle the correct **adverb**.

Does a snail move _____ than a turtle?

slowly   more slowly   most slowly

Maybe the snail is moving _____ than an ant.

quickly   more quickly   most quickly

But which of the three animals can move _____?

quickly   more quickly   most quickly

The rabbit thought the turtle went _____.

slowly   more slowly   most slowly

But the turtle raced _____ than the rabbit!

cleverly   more cleverly   most cleverly

Skills: Comparing with adverbs

GRAMMAR

The name of a book is called the title.
The first word and all the important words in a title begin with capital letters.

The following words are not capitalized in titles:

a	an	and	for	in	of	on	the	to

Handwritten titles should be underlined.

Rewrite each title correctly on the line.

The cat in the hat _____

The little princess _____

bread and jam for Frances _____

snow white and rose red _____

Write the title of your favorite book.

_____

Skills: Capitalization of titles

You can use an apostrophe to join two words that are often used together. The apostrophe takes the place of a letter or letters that are left out. These combined words are called **contractions**.

I + will = I'll
The apostrophe stands for **wi**.

Circle the letters that are replaced by the apostrophe.

I + am = I'm

We + will = we'll

They + have = they've

You + are = you're

Skills: Forming contractions with **to be** and **to have**

GRAMMAR

A **contraction** is a word made up of two short words and an apostrophe (').
The apostrophe takes the place of a letter or letters that are left out of the
words. Here are some you use a lot:

I'm	**=**	**I am**
isn't	**=**	**is not**
can't	**=**	**can not**
she's	**=**	**she is**

What letter does the apostrophe replace in **I am**? _____

What letter does the apostrophe replace in **is not**? _____

What letters does the apostrophe replace in **can not**? _____

What letter does the apostrophe replace in **she is**? _____

Draw lines to match the words with their contractions.

you are   we're

should have   I'll

we are   they're

I will   you're

they are   should've

Skills: Understanding contractions

182

GRAMMAR

You can also make contractions with not.

> **Have + not = haven't**
> **Can + not = can't**

One contraction has a strange spelling.

> **Will + not = won't**

haven't	don't	wasn't
can't	isn't	doesn't
won't	aren't	couldn't

Fill in the correct **contraction** from the word box.

It _____ time for the game yet.
  is not

Mary _____ care who wins, but I do.
       does not

The teams _____ taken the field.
           have not

Jack likes the Tigers, but they _____
very good.   are not

If we _____ score soon, we _____ win.
      do not   will not

Skills: Forming and using contractions with not

183

GRAMMAR

Color only the spaces that have **contractions**. What do you see?
Now color the rest of the picture.

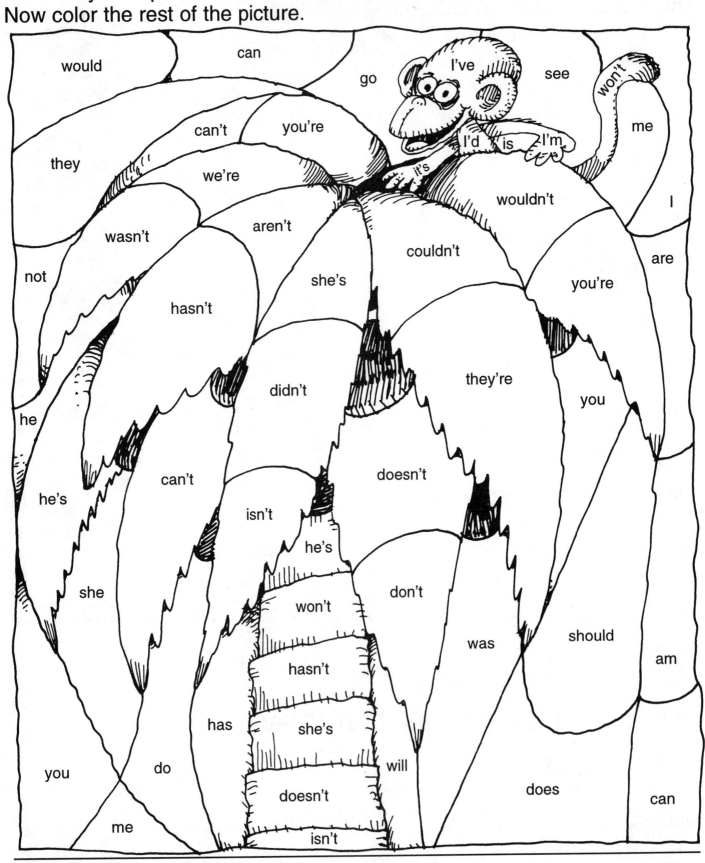

Skills: Identifying contractions

GRAMMAR

Make new words. Add a new beginning consonant to a word-family ending. The words rhyme because they end with the same sound.

Read the words in each word family. Write one more word for each family.

Some common word families:

_ake	_at	_ing	_and	_ide
make	bat	sing	band	hide
bake	sat	wing	hand	ride
_____	_____	_____	_____	_____

Now write a new word for each word family below.
Circle the letters of the family name.

hug _____

bit _____

win _____

day _____

top _____

hang _____

Skills: Spelling words in word families

GRAMMAR

Did you know that **y** has a **long e** sound at the end of some words?

Find these **y** words across or down in the puzzle:

BABY	**BUNNY**	**FUNNY**	**WINDY**
VERY	**PENNY**	**PRETTY**	**TINY**
SANDY	**SILLY**	**REALLY**	**WEARY**

```
S Q J P R E T T Y T
I X R E A L L Y W I
L B U N N Y P Q I N
L A Z N X F U N N Y
Y B L Y V E R Y D X
Y Y S A N D Y X Y Z
B O E W E A R Y N A
```

Skills: Spelling words ending in y

GRAMMAR

The **long a** sound may be spelled **a**, **ai**, or **ay**.

Circle all the words with the **long a** sound.

The train came to the station.

I hope it wasn't late.

Is it going to rain today?

If it does, the mail will be late.

Stay right here.

Don't wait for me in Watertown.

Amy wants to paint on the train!

Skills: Spelling the long a sound

GRAMMAR

The **long e** sound can be spelled **e**, **ea**, **ee**, or **y** (at the end of a word).

Color in only the spaces that have a word with the **long e** sound.

Skills: Spelling the long e sound

GRAMMAR

The **long i** sound can be spelled **i**, **ie**, **y**, or **igh**.

night	tie	eye	find
why	high	mine	pie
	might	right	

Read each clue. Write the answers in the puzzle. Each answer is a word that has a **long i** sound. Use the word box if you need help.

Down

1. Could
3. Belonging to me
4. Opposite of left
5. How come
6. Dessert with a crust

Across

2. Opposite of lose
7. Opposite of low
8. Opposite of day
9. What you see with
10. Fasten a shoelace

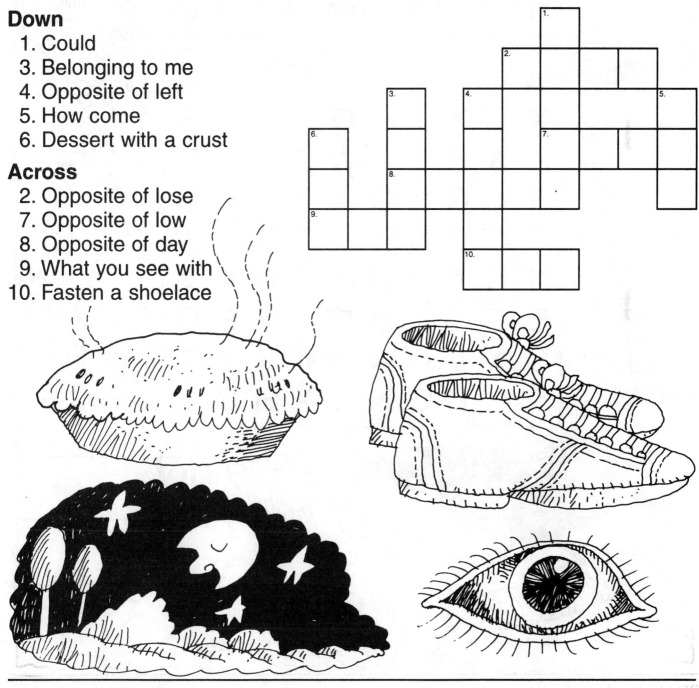

Skills: Spelling the long i sound

GRAMMAR

The **long o** sound can be spelled **o**, **oa**, **oe**, or **ow**.

Look across, down, and diagonally to find these words with the **long o** sound:

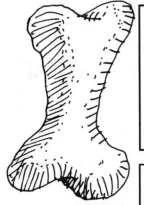

ALONE	BOAT	BONE	CROW	GO
GOAT	GROW	HOE	KNOW	LOW
MOAN	OATS	OPEN	PHONE	ROW
SOAP	SOW	STONE	THRONE	
THROW	TOE	VOTE	WOE	WROTE

```
W R O T E S O A P T
X C X Y G O P E N H
Z A R Z R W O E P R
B L G O O A T S H O
O O O K W S T R O W
N N A O N T J O N V
E E T T M O A N E O
Q X L O W N W E X T
T H R O N E X H O E
```

Skills: Spelling the long o sound

GRAMMAR

All of these words have the **long u** sound, spelled **oo** or **ue**.
But the letters are all mixed up! Can you unscramble them?
Use the word box if you need to check spellings.

clue	food	blue
spoon	room	moon
balloon	noon	true

nomo _____

leub _____

dofo _____

leuc _____

moor _____

ture _____

snopo _____

lonbloa _____

onon _____

Skills: Spelling the long u sound

GRAMMAR

Make new words by adding –**ing** at the end of a verb.
If the verb ends in **e**, drop the **e** before adding –**ing**.

call	call**ing**
bak**e**	bak**ing**

smiling	**hiding**	**playing**
going	**reading**	**skating**
thinking	**snowing**	**sleeping**

Write an –**ing** word to complete each sentence. Use the word box if you need help with spelling.

The ice is thick, so let's go _____.

Shh! The baby's _____.

You make me happy, so I'm _____.

The sun is _____ behind the clouds.

I can use my new sled because it's _____!

I'm _____ the most exciting book.

Have you been _____ it over?

You should be _____ to bed!

He's been _____ baseball for years.

Skills: Spelling verbs with the –ing ending

GRAMMAR

Double the final consonants of some verbs before adding **–ing** or **–ed**.

> nap napped napping

Read each clue. Write each word with the **–ed** or **–ing** ending. Use the word box if you need help.

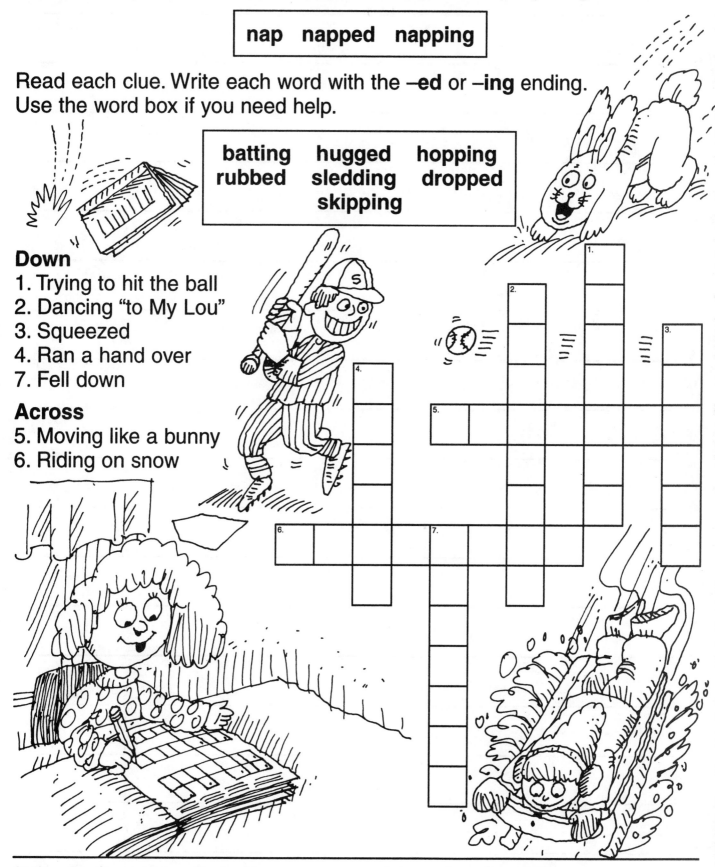

> batting hugged hopping
> rubbed sledding dropped
> skipping

Down
1. Trying to hit the ball
2. Dancing "to My Lou"
3. Squeezed
4. Ran a hand over
7. Fell down

Across
5. Moving like a bunny
6. Riding on snow

Skills: Spelling words with double consonants and the –ed or –ing ending

PRACTICE PAGE

DICTIONARY

How to Use This Book

This dictionary is written to help you get to know words: learn their meanings, check their spellings, and see how they can be used in a sentence. The word entries are in alphabetical order (see exercises on p. 197). After each word you can find out what part of speech it is. This is followed by a definition of the word. Finally, to make the meaning clearer, you can read a sentence using that word. Look at the sample page below. The diagram will explain how to use the entries in this dictionary.

Each page begins with an upper and lowercase letter. All the words in that section begin with this letter.

An entry word is the word that is being defined. It is in dark type.

The part of speech tells what a word does in a sentence. (See the guide to Parts of Speech on page 196.)

The definition tells what the word means.

An example sentence shows how each entry word can be used in a sentence.

A picture can help to show what a word means.

All the words on the page are in alphabetical order. For example, the word *alligator* comes before the word *among* because *al* comes before *am*.

Aa

across *adverb, preposition* Across means from one side to another.
He walked across *the room.*

advertise *verb* To advertise is to tell about something that you are selling.
Tommy wants the game he saw advertised *in the magazine.*

again *adverb* Again means one more time.
Jane played the computer game again *and again.*

airplane *noun* An airplane is a flying machine that has engines and wings.
The airplane *flew from Boston to Chicago.*

alligator *noun* An alligator is an animal in the reptile family with short legs.
The alligator *looks similar to a crocodile.*

among *preposition* Among means between more than two people, or in the middle of.
Jenny divides the apples among *her three friends.*

anchor *noun* An anchor is a heavy piece of metal used for keeping a boat in one place.
We dropped the anchor *out of the boat.*

ancient *adjective* Ancient means very old.
The pyramids are ancient *ruins.*

angry *adjective* Angry means feeling annoyed or mad.
Paul was angry *at Sue for breaking his toy.*

ant *noun* An ant is a tiny insect.
Look at the ants *near that anthill.*

apple *noun* An apple is a fruit that grows on trees.
Do you like green apples?

armor *noun* Armor is something worn for protection in battle.
The knight's metal armor *was heavy.*

astronaut *noun* An astronaut explores outer space.
The astronauts *boarded the spacecraft.*

Can you write a sentence using a word from this page?

_____

_____

_____

Parts of Speech

Next to each entry in this dictionary is the name of a part of speech. The part of speech tells how a word should be used in a sentence. Read on to learn about each part of speech. Then read each sentence to see how each part of speech can be used.

noun – A noun is the name of a person, a place, or a thing.
Sam and Dave got a really great video at the drug store on Main Street.

pronoun – A pronoun takes the place of a noun in a sentence.
They watched it at Sam's house. His TV is bigger than Dave's.

adjective – An adjective is a word that describes a noun or a pronoun.
The video was funny but scary. They thought it was a good movie.

verb – A verb is a word that refers to an action or a state of being.
Sam jumped up during the scary part. Then, he ate popcorn and drank soda.

adverb – An adverb is a word that describes a verb, an adjective, or another adverb.
Sam and Dave screamed loudly at the very scary parts but laughed heartily at the end.

conjunction – A conjunction is a word that joins words or connects phrases.
Sam and Dave went back to the video store but didn't get another movie.

preposition – A preposition is a word that connects one noun or noun equivalent to another in the same sentence.
Dave watched the movie with Sam. Dave went home after it was finished.

interjection – An interjection is a word that expresses strong feeling.
Yikes! That scene was scary. Wow! That movie was great.

Can You Alphabetize?

Words in the dictionary are in alphabetical order. Practice your alphabetizing skills by putting the words in each row in alphabetical order. Write a 1, 2, or 3 to show the correct alphabetical order of the words.

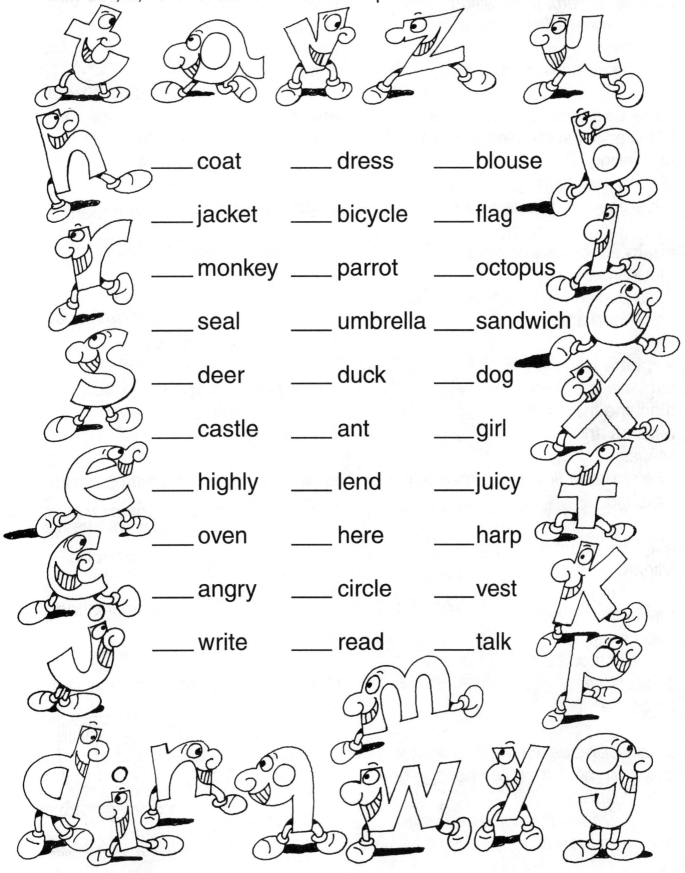

____ coat ____ dress ____ blouse

____ jacket ____ bicycle ____ flag

____ monkey ____ parrot ____ octopus

____ seal ____ umbrella ____ sandwich

____ deer ____ duck ____ dog

____ castle ____ ant ____ girl

____ highly ____ lend ____ juicy

____ oven ____ here ____ harp

____ angry ____ circle ____ vest

____ write ____ read ____ talk

Aa

across *adverb, preposition*
Across means from one side
to another.
He walked across *the room.*

advertise *verb* To advertise is
to tell about something that you
are selling.
Tommy wants the game he saw
advertised *in the magazine.*

again *adverb* Again means one
more time.
Jane played the computer game
again *and* again.

airplane *noun* An
airplane is a flying
machine that has
engines and
wings.

The airplane *flew from Boston to
Chicago.*

alligator *noun* An
alligator is an
animal in the
reptile family with
short legs.
The alligator *looks
similar to a
crocodile.*

among *preposition* Among means
between more than two people, or
in the middle of.
Jenny divides the apples among
her three friends.

anchor *noun* An
anchor is a heavy
piece of metal
used for keeping a
boat in one place.
*We dropped the
anchor* out of
the boat.

ancient *adjective* Ancient means
very old.
The pyramids are ancient *ruins.*

angry *adjective* Angry means
feeling annoyed or mad.
Paul was angry *at Sue for
breaking his toy.*

ant *noun* An ant is a tiny insect.
Look at the ants *near that anthill.*

apple *noun* An apple is a fruit that
grows on trees.
Do you like green apples?

armor *noun* Armor is something
worn for protection in battle.
The knight's metal armor *was heavy.*

astronaut *noun* An astronaut
explores outer space.
The astronauts *boarded the
spacecraft.*

Can you write a sentence using a
word from this page?

_____

_____

_____

baby *noun* A baby is a very young child.
That baby *is so cute!*

ball *noun* A ball is a round toy used for sports.
Throw me the ball!

bake *verb* To bake is to cook in an oven.
Mom bakes *the best cakes.*

banana *noun* A banana is a long, curved yellow fruit.

Do you like apples or bananas?

bear *noun* A bear is a large furry animal.
Bears *sleep through the winter.*

beautiful *adjective* Something that is lovely to look at is beautiful.
The flowers in the garden are beautiful.

bend *verb* To bend something is to change its shape.
You can bend *wire into many shapes.*

beneath *preposition* Beneath means below; under.
The newspaper is beneath *the book.*

beside *preposition* Beside means next to.
Put the pencil beside *the notebook.*

Bb

bicycle *noun* Bicycles are machines with two wheels, used for riding.
Can I ride my bicycle *to school?*

box *noun* A box is a rectangular container.
I put the gift in a box.

boy *noun* A boy is a male child.
Stephen is a new boy *in our class.*

bull *noun* A bull is a male cow.
Bulls *have sharp horns.*

butterfly *noun* A butterfly is an insect with brightly colored wings.

Look at that orange butterfly.

buy *verb* To buy is to purchase or pay for something.
I want to buy *a new book.*

Can you write a sentence using a word from this page?

_____

_____

_____

Cc

cake *noun* A cake is a dessert usually made using flour, sugar, and eggs.
We baked a birthday cake *for you.*

camera *noun* A camera is a small machine used for taking pictures.
You can take a picture with your new camera.

carry *verb* To carry is to pick something up and take it somewhere.
Are those books too heavy for you to carry?

castle *noun* A castle is a large stone fortress where kings and queens lived hundreds of years ago.
We are going to see the king's castle.

catch *verb* To catch is to take hold of something while it is moving.
Can Max catch *the ball?*

cheerfully *adverb* Cheerfully means in a happy way.
Kim cheerfully *picked the flowers.*

chicken *noun* A chicken is a bird that lives on a farm and lays eggs.
That chicken *laid many eggs.*

circle *noun* A circle is a flat, round shape.
The face of the clock is a circle.

clever *adjective* Clever means smart or able to learn quickly.
The girl was quite clever *at working puzzles.*

clock *noun* A clock is an instrument used for telling time.
Tell me what time the clock *shows.*

corn *noun* Corn is a type of vegetable that grows on a stalk.
The corn *we had at dinner was tasty.*

crooked *adjective* Crooked means bent; not straight.
The branch on the tree was very crooked.

crow *noun* A crow is a type of black bird.
The straw man didn't really scare the crows.

Can you write a sentence using a word from this page?

_____

_____

_____

dance *verb* To dance is to move your body to music.
Beth dances *very gracefully.*

deer *noun* A deer is a brown furry animal that lives in the forest and runs fast.
The deer *stood very still in the woods.*

delicate *adjective* Delicate means fragile or finely worked.
Be careful; that lace is delicate.

delicious *adjective* Delicious means tasty to eat.
This sandwich is delicious.

desk *noun* A desk is a piece of furniture that people sit at to write.
Put your papers on the desk.

dessert *noun* Dessert is a sweet food that is usually served at the end of a meal.
Do you want cookies or ice cream for dessert?

dinosaur *noun* A dinosaur is a huge prehistoric animal that lived millions of years ago. Dinosaurs *are extinct.*

dirty *adjective* Dirty means smudged with dirt; not clean.
Pat's clothes were dirty.

dive *verb* To dive is to jump in with your arms and head first.
Let's dive *into the swimming pool.*

doctor *noun* A doctor is person who takes care of people's health.
I go to the doctor *when I am sick.*

doll *noun* A doll is a toy in the shape of a person.
Jane loves her baby doll.

down *preposition* Down means towards a lower position; the opposite of up.
The leaf fell down *to the ground.*

drum *noun* A drum is a musical instrument that you bang to make beats or sounds.
He beat the drum *very hard.*

duck *noun* A duck is a bird that flies in the air and swims in the water.
The mother duck *led the ducklings.*

Can you write a sentence using a word from this page?

_____

_____

Ee

eagle *noun* An eagle is a large, powerful bird of prey.
The eagle has large wings.

egg *noun* An egg is a hard oval shell from which baby chicks hatch.
There are twelve eggs in the carton.

eight *noun* Eight is a number that is one more than seven.
Tom wears number eight for his softball team.

either *conjunction* Either means one or the other of two things.
I want either milk or juice.

elbow *noun* The joint that allows the arm to bend is called an elbow.
Can you bend your elbow?

elephant *noun* An elephant is a very large gray animal with a long trunk. Elephants *come from Africa and Asia.*

enter *verb* To enter is to go into.
Be quiet as you enter the library.

especially *adverb* Especially means most of all.
I especially like chocolate.

except *preposition* Except means besides; other than.
I like all the shirts except this one.

exclaim *verb* To exclaim is to say something loudly and with excitement.
"This is wonderful!" exclaimed Sara.

expensive *adjective* Expensive means high-priced; costing a great deal of money.
It was a very expensive painting.

extra *adjective* Extra means added to the usual.
He gave me an extra blanket in case it got cold.

extremely *adverb* Extremely means to a great degree.
He is extremely smart.

eye *noun* An eye is a body part that helps you to see. People have two eyes.
You use your eyes to see.

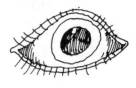

Can you write a sentence using a word from this page?

_____

_____

_____

famous *adjective* Famous means known by many people. *We saw a* famous *actor at the market.*

farmer *noun* A farmer is a person who grows crops or raises animals on a farm. *The* farmer *grew corn and beans.*

fantastic *adjective* Fantastic means amazing; wonderful. *The music at the party was* fantastic.

feather *noun* A feather is a piece of the soft outer covering on a bird. *The bird had green* feathers.

fence *noun* A fence is a barrier made out of wood or metal, used to mark or block off an area. *The* fence *is tall and wide.*

finish *verb* To finish is to come to the end of something. *I* finished *my homework.*

fish *noun* A fish is an animal that lives in the water and breathes through gills. *There are many* fish *in the pond.*

flag *noun* A flag is a piece of colored fabric attached to a pole, often symbolizing a nation. *The* flag *waved in the breeze.*

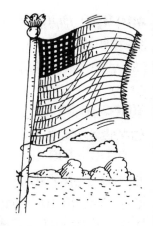

for *conjunction* For connects two nouns with reference to purpose. *I will bring drinks* for *the party at school tomorrow.*

frog *noun* A frog is a small amphibian that uses its back legs for jumping. *The* frog *jumped onto the lily pad.*

from *preposition* From can mean out of or because of. *Lemonade is made* from *lemons.*

fruit *noun* A fruit is a part of a plant that contains seeds or a pit. Many fruits are edible. *The pie is made from fresh* fruit.

Can you write a sentence using a word from this page?

_____

_____

_____

Ff

Gg

garage *noun* A garage is a building where cars are kept.
There are two cars in our garage.

garden *noun* A garden is a plot of land that is used to grow flowers or vegetables.
We planted roses in our garden.

gate *noun* A gate is a door in a fence or a wall.
The gate *to our yard was open.*

gently *adverb* Gently means mildly.
Samantha gently *strokes the rabbit's fur.*

gift *noun* A gift is something given from one person to another.
Liz brought a gift *for you.*

giraffe *noun* A giraffe is a tall African animal with a long neck.
We saw a giraffe *in the zoo.*

girl *noun* A girl is a female child.
That girl *has very long hair.*

glow *verb* To glow is to shine with continuous light.
The lamplight glowed *above us.*

goat *noun* A goat is a four-legged animal with horns.
The goat *wanted to be fed.*

gorgeous *adjective* Gorgeous means very beautiful.
That necklace is gorgeous.

grab *verb* To grab is to take hold of something roughly and quickly.
He grabbed *the ball from Jake.*

grouchy *adjective* Grouchy means in a bad mood.
Jon was grouchy *in the morning.*

grow *verb* To grow is to get bigger.
Sunshine makes flowers grow.

growl *verb* To growl is to make a deep, rough noise in the throat.
The dog growled *when he heard a noise.*

guitar *noun* A guitar is a musical instrument with six strings.
David likes to play the guitar.

Can you write a sentence using a word from this page?

_____

_____

_____

_____

hammer *noun* A hammer is a tool with a long handle and a heavy head for banging.
I brought a hammer *and nails.*

harp *noun* A harp is a musical instrument with a large frame and strings. *Melissa plays the* harp.

hairy *adjective* Hairy means covered with hair.
The hairy *monster in the story scared us.*

hay *noun* Hay is grass that has been cut and dried for animals to eat.
The horses ate so much hay.

helicopter *noun* A helicopter is an aircraft that has a propeller on top instead of wings. *We wanted to ride in the* helicopter.

here *adverb* Here means in this place.
Our friends will meet us here.

hey *interjection* Hey is usually said to get someone's attention.
Hey, *we are over here!*

hide *verb* To hide is to place out of sight; conceal.
Hide *the presents in the closet.*

hill *noun* A hill is an area of raised ground.
Jack and Jill went up the hill.

hippopotamus *noun* A hippopotamus is a large gray animal with short legs and a large mouth. *The* hippopotamus *stayed in the water.*

horse *noun* A horse is a four-legged animal with a long tail and a mane.
I like to ride the brown horse.

hug *verb* To hug is to put your arms tightly around another person.
The mother hugs *her baby.*

hunger *noun* Hunger is the need or desire for food.
Many people suffer from hunger *every day.*

hurt *verb* To hurt is to cause pain.
I scraped my knee, and it hurts!

Can you write a sentence using a word from this page?

_____

_____

_____

Ii

ice *noun* Ice is frozen water.
The ice *is cold and hard.*

ice cream *noun*
Ice cream is a
frozen dessert
made from cream
and sugar.
I like vanilla ice
cream.

if *conjunction* If
means supposing that.
You will get wet if *you go out in
the rain.*

igloo *noun* An
igloo is a house
made of blocks of
hard snow and ice.
*Eskimos live
in* igloos.

imaginary
adjective Imaginary means
make-believe.
*Stephen likes to play with
imaginary friends.*

immediately *adverb* Immediately
means right now.
We must go immediately *to the
doctor's office.*

impossible *adjective* Impossible
means not able to be done or
to happen.
It is impossible *for pigs to fly.*

insect *noun* An insect is a tiny
animal with six legs, such as
an ant or bee.
Butterflies are the prettiest insects.

inside *preposition* Inside means
within; enclosed in.
Your heart is inside *your body.*

invent *verb* To invent means to
create something that did not
exist before.
Do you know who invented
the airplane?

iron *noun* An iron
is a hard metal
tool that is heated
to take the
wrinkles out of
clothes.
Use the iron *to
take the wrinkles
out of your shirt.*

island *noun* An island is a piece
of land surrounded by water.
Let's swim to the island!

ivy *noun* Ivy is a kind of green plant
that often grows on walls and gates.
*The walls of the library are
covered with* ivy.

Can you write a sentence using a
word from this page?

_____

_____

_____

jacket *noun* A jacket is a short coat.
Put on your winter jacket.

jar *noun* A jar is a glass container with a wide mouth.
We put pickles in the big jar.

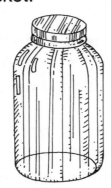

jelly *noun* Jelly is a kind of smooth spread made out fruit.
I want jelly *on my sandwich.*

jet *noun* A jet is a very fast airplane.
We flew on a jumbo jet.

jewelry *noun* Jewelry is decorative things people wear, such as rings, bracelets, necklaces and earrings.
That store sells pretty jewelry.

jog *verb* To jog is to trot.
My sister jogs *each morning.*

jointly *adverb* Jointly means together; as a group.
We jointly *own a lemonade stand.*

journal *noun* A journal is a book in which you write your thoughts every day.
My sister keeps a journal.

Jj

judge *noun* A judge is a person in charge of a trial.
The judge *called for order.*

juggle *verb* To juggle is to toss several things up in the air and catch them one at a time so one or more things are in the air at all times.
My brother can juggle *balls and pins.*

juicy *adjective* Juicy means filled with juice.
The oranges were really juicy.

jump *verb* To jump is to push your body up so that your feet do not touch the ground.
When you play hopscotch, you have to jump.

jungle *noun* The jungle is a dense tropical forest where animals like monkeys live.
It's easy to get lost in the jungle.

Can you write a sentence using a word from this page?

_____

_____

_____

Kk

kangaroo *noun* A kangaroo is a large Australian animal that uses its powerful tail to jump.
Female kangaroos *carry their babies in pouches.*

key *noun* A key is a flat piece of metal that opens and closes a lock.
Use the key *to unlock the door.*

kick *verb* To kick is to hit with your foot.
He kicked *the soccer ball to score a goal.*

kid *noun* A kid is a young goat.
The kids *played in the meadow.*

kind *adjective* Kind means considerate of the feelings of others.
She is kind *to animals.*

king *noun* A king is a man who rules his country.
The king *sat on his throne.*

kiss *verb* To kiss is to touch affectionately with the lips.
My mother always kisses *me goodnight.*

kitchen *noun* A kitchen is a room where food is cooked.
We cooked dinner in the kitchen.

kite *noun* A kite is a flat toy on a string that flies in the wind.
Look at the kite *stuck in that tree.*

kneel *verb* To kneel is to go down on one's knees.
I had to kneel *to find my lost ring.*

knight *noun* A knight was a soldier who wore armor and lived in a castle in feudal times.
The knight *was very brave.*

knock *verb* To knock is to hit with your fist.
He knocked *on the front door.*

knowingly *adverb* Knowingly means on purpose; deliberately.
He knowingly *took the wrong book.*

koala *noun* A koala is a small Australian animal that looks like a little gray bear.
That koala *is so cute.*

Can you write a sentence using a word from this page?

_____

_____

_____

ladder *noun* A ladder is two long poles with rungs between them, used for climbing.
He climbed up the ladder *to get to the roof.*

ladybug *noun* A ladybug is a small round beetle that is usually red with black dots on it.

The ladybug *crawled onto the leaf.*

large *adjective* Large means big.
That is a large *rock.*

late *adverb* Late means after the appointed time.
She was late *to the party.*

lazy *adjective* Lazy means without energy; not willing to work.
She was too lazy *to make her bed.*

leaf *noun* A leaf is the thin flat part of a plant that absorbs sunlight.
The leaf *fell off the tree.*

leap *verb* To leap is to jump.
A frog can leap *from lily pad to lily pad.*

lemon *noun* A lemon is a yellow fruit that has a sour taste.
I like lemon *in my tea.*

lend *verb* To lend is to let someone borrow.
Can you lend *me your baseball mitt?*

like *preposition* Like means the same as or similar to.
A softball is somewhat like *a baseball, but bigger and softer.*

lion *noun* A lion is a large wild cat.
The lion *is very fierce.*

little *adjective* Little means small.
The little *boy is near his big brother.*

lock *noun* A lock is a device used to keep an object such as a door or box closed.
Put the lock *on the box.*

loudly *adverb* Loudly means in a noisy way.
He called loudly *for everyone to join him.*

love *verb* To love is to like a lot; to feel affection.
I love *my mother.*

Can you write a sentence using a word from this page?

_____

_____

_____

Mm

mail *noun* Mail is letters, postcards and packages sent from one person to another.
The mail *comes at ten o'clock each morning.*

mainly *adverb* Mainly means for the most part.
I work mainly *in the office but sometimes I work at home.*

majestically *adverb* Majestically means in a grand or noble manner.
The king walked majestically *through the town.*

map *noun* A map is a drawing that shows what an area looks like from above.
The map *showed all fifty states.*

march *verb* To march is to walk in even, rhythmic steps.
Soldiers marched *in the parade.*

memorize *verb* To memorize is to study something in order to remember it.
He memorized *his lines for the class play.*

messy *adjective* Messy means untidy or sloppy.
Matt's room was really messy.

milk *noun* Milk is a white liquid that comes from female mammals such as cows.

Stephen likes to drink tall glasses of milk.

miserable *adjective* Miserable means very unhappy.
She was miserable *because she couldn't go to the party.*

monkey *noun* A monkey is an animal with long arms and a very flexible tail.
The monkey *hung by his tail.*

motorcycle *noun* A motorcycle is a vehicle with two wheels and a motor.
Ben likes to ride his motorcycle.

mouse *noun* A mouse is a tiny animal with sharp teeth and a long tail.
The mouse *ran across the room.*

mushroom *noun* A mushroom is a fungus, often edible, shaped like an umbrella.
He likes mushrooms *on his pizza.*

Can you write a sentence using a word from this page?

_____

_____

_____

napkin *noun* A napkin is a cloth or paper used for wiping fingers and mouths.
Please put your napkin *on your lap.*

narrow *adjective* Narrow means thin from side to side; not wide.
The river is narrow *here.*

near *preposition* Near means close to.
I want to sit near *Judy.*

nearly *adverb* Nearly means almost but not quite.
It is nearly *bedtime.*

necklace *noun* A necklace is a piece of jewelry that you wear around your neck.
I like the green necklace.

needle *noun* A needle is a thin piece of metal that can be threaded and used for sewing.
I can sew with a needle *and thread.*

nest *noun* A nest is a home for birds made of grass, twigs, and other things.
The red bird lives in that nest.

net *noun* A net is a surface made of knotted rope, used to catch things.
Did you catch fish in your net?

never *adverb* Never means not ever.
I never *want to do that again!*

newspaper *noun* A newspaper is a publication consisting of stories and pictures about current events.
I bought you today's newspaper.

nickel *noun* A nickel is a type of coin that is worth five cents.
That gum costs a nickel.

nine *noun* Nine is a number that is one more than eight.
Nine *is one less than ten.*

notify *verb* To notify is to let someone know.
Please notify *me when Jay comes.*

now *adverb* Now means at this moment; immediately.
Come in now.

nut *noun* A nut is a fruit with a hard shell that grows on a tree.
The squirrels like to eat nuts.

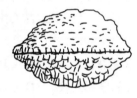

Can you write a sentence using a word from this page?

_____

_____

_____

Oo

oar *noun* An oar is a long paddle used for rowing a boat.
Make sure the oars *are the same length.*

obey *verb* To obey is to listen or do as one is told.
The driver must obey *the traffic light.*

octopus *noun* An octopus is a sea animal with eight tentacles.
We saw an octopus *at the aquarium.*

old *adjective* Old means aged; not young or new.
I will wear my old *shoes in the rain.*

olive *noun* An olive is a small green or black fruit that has a pit.
Do you want olives *in your salad?*

once *adverb* Once means one time or at an earlier time.
I have been to a ballgame once *before.*

onion *noun* An onion is an edible bulb with a very strong taste and smell.
The onion *gives this flavor.*

or *conjunction* Or refers to a choice between two things.
Do you want vanilla or *chocolate ice cream?*

outside *preposition* Outside means out of or beyond the limit of.
Please play softball outside *the house.*

oval *noun* An oval is a rounded, oblong shape.
This mirror is an oval.

oven *noun* An oven is a machine used for baking and broiling.
She baked the pie in the oven.

over *preposition* Over means above.
The plane flew too low over *our house.*

owl *noun* An owl is a type of bird that sleeps during the day.
The owl *hooted all night long.*

own *verb* To own is to possess; when you own something, it belongs to you.
I own *three of those shirts.*

Can you write a sentence using a word from this page?

_____

_____

_____

pail *noun* A pail is a container used to carry things in.
Take the pail *and shovel to the beach.*

pajamas *noun* Pajamas are clothing that people wear while they sleep.
I am wearing my bunny pajamas.

palace *noun* A palace is a large, fancy home with many rooms.
We will visit the royal palace.

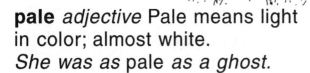

pale *adjective* Pale means light in color; almost white.
She was as pale *as a ghost.*

pancake *noun* A pancake is a thin, flat breakfast food made from flour, eggs and milk.
I like blueberry pancakes.

panda *noun* A panda is a black and white bearlike mammal that comes from China.
Pandas *only like to eat bamboo shoots.*

parrot *noun* A parrot is a colorful bird with a curved beak. Parrots can be taught to speak.
My cousin has a pet parrot *named Polly.*

past *preposition* Past means beyond.
The bus went past *the bus stop.*

piano *noun* A piano is a large musical instrument with a long row of black and white keys.
There is a piano *in the living room.*

pint *noun* A pint is a unit of liquid measure.
The recipe calls for a pint *of cream.*

polish *verb* To polish is to rub something until it shines.
Henry polished *his shoes.*

pot *noun* A pot is a deep round pan used for cooking.
I will make soup in this pot.

pretty *adjective* Pretty means attractive to the eye.
He saw a pretty *girl at the show.*

Can you write a sentence using a word from this page?

_____

_____

_____

Qq

quack *noun* Quack is the sound that a duck makes.
We heard the quack *of the duck in the water.*

quaint *adjective* Quaint means unusual in a pleasing way.
The house in the country was quaint *and interesting.*

quarrel *verb* To quarrel is to argue.
I quarreled *with my brother yesterday.*

quart *noun* A quart is a unit of liquid measure equal to two pints.
Buy a quart *of milk.*

quarter *noun* A quarter is a kind of coin worth twenty-five cents.
I need a quarter *for the gumball machine.*

queen *noun* A queen is a woman who rules a country.
The queen *wore a crown.*

question mark *noun* A question mark is symbol used at the end of a sentence that asks a question.
The teacher reminded me to

put a question mark *at the end of the sentence.*

quickly *adverb* Quickly means rapidly.
We ran quickly *to the car.*

quill *noun* A quill is a large stiff feather, often used for writing.
He signed his name with a quill *pen.*

quilt *noun* A quilt is a soft, fluffy cover for a bed.
The quilt *was handmade by my grandmother.*

quip *noun* A quip is a quick joke or pun.
Everyone laughs at his quips.

quite *adverb* Quite means rather or somewhat.
I am quite *tired.*

quiver *verb* To quiver is to shiver or shake.
She was quivering *when she came out of the cold water.*

Can you write a sentence using a word from this page?

_____

_____

_____

rabbit *noun* A rabbit is a small, furry, long-eared animal that hops from place to place.
The rabbit *hopped through the garden*

rainbow *noun* A rainbow is an arc of colored light that can sometimes be seen in the sky.
I saw a beautiful rainbow *after the storm.*

rarely *adverb* Rarely means not often or seldom.
We rarely *see these friends.*

raw *adjective* Raw means uncooked or unprepared.
The meat was raw *before we cooked it.*

rehearse *verb* To rehearse is to practice.
We will rehearse *the magic act tomorrow.*

return *verb* To return is to give back or go back.
I will return *to my desk.*

rhinoceros *noun* A rhinoceros is a large animal with one or two large horns on its nose.
The rhinoceros *has thick skin.*

ring *noun* A ring is a type of jewelry worn on one's finger.
I left my ring *on the table.*

river *noun* A river is a path of water that flows toward the sea.
The river *was wide and deep.*

roast *verb* To roast is to cook in the oven.
We roasted *a turkey for dinner.*

robot *noun* A robot is a machine that is built to do the jobs that people usually do.
The robot *was three feet tall.*

rude *adjective* Rude means impolite; ill-behaved.
The man was rude *to my friend.*

rug *noun* A rug is a floor covering made from wool or cloth.
We bought a new rug *for our home.*

Can you write a sentence using a word from this page?

_____

_____

_____

Ss

saddle *noun* A saddle is a seat for a rider on a horse.
He sat up straight in the saddle.

sandwich *noun* A sandwich is food between two slices of bread.
I want a turkey sandwich *rather than a hamburger.*

say *verb* To say is to speak; put into words.
Did he say *where he was going?*

scissors *noun* Scissors are small sharp tools used for cutting paper or cloth.
I will cut the paper dolls out with scissors.

scribble *verb* To scribble is to write quickly and in a messy way.
The child scribbled *on the paper.*

seal *noun* A seal is a sea mammal that has thick brown fur and flippers.
We watched the man feed the seals.

seldom *adverb* Seldom means rarely; not often.
We seldom *get to see our cousins.*

shark *noun* A shark is a very large fish that has sharp teeth and a large mouth.
We saw a shark *in the aquarium.*

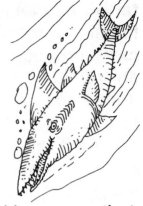

sled *noun* A sled is a small flat toy with runners that people use to ride down snowy hills.
Larry took his sled *to the park.*

small *adjective* Small means little; not large.
We have a small *dog.*

snake *noun* A snake is a reptile with no legs and a long narrow body.
The snake *slithered through the forest.*

spider *noun* A spider is a small eight-legged animal that spins webs to catch insects.
The spider *was making a web.*

still *adverb* Still means even at this time.
I still *believe that wishes come true.*

Can you write a sentence using a word from this page?

_____

_____

_____

table *noun* A table is a piece of furniture with a flat top that you can put things on.
Put the flowers on the table.

tent *noun* A tent is a portable shelter made from poles, rope, and fabric.
We can sleep in the tent.

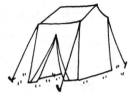

terrible *adjective* Terrible means very bad or unpleasant.
There was a terrible *rainstorm last night.*

there *adverb* There means in that place.
I will sit there.

think *verb* To think is to have ideas or thoughts.
I often think *about outer space.*

timid *adjective* Timid means shy or easily frightened.
Deer are timid *animals.*

tire *noun* A tire is a tube of rubber that goes around a wheel.
We had to change the tire *on our car.*

tomato *noun* A tomato is a type of soft fruit that is red or green.
I will put a tomato *in the salad.*

tomb *noun* A tomb is a place to bury the dead.
King Tut's tomb *was filled with treasures.*

towel *noun* A towel is a large piece of soft material used for drying.
Please give me a towel.

train *noun* A train is a set of railroad or subway cars that move along a track.
We will take a train *to the city.*

tree *noun* A tree is a large plant with a thick wooden stem.
My cat is stuck in the tree.

trip *verb* To trip is to stumble.
I tripped on my shoelace.

truck *noun* A truck is a large vehicle that carries animals or objects from place to place.
The truck *will bring the package.*

turtle *noun* A turtle is a small reptile with a hard outer shell.
The turtle *pulled its head into its shell.*

Can you write a sentence using a word from this page?

_____

_____

_____

Uu

ugly *adjective* Ugly means unattractive; not pretty.
That sculpture is so ugly.

umbrella *noun* An umbrella is a folding device held above the head to keep dry in the rain.
I have a green and blue umbrella.

uncle *noun* Your uncle is your mother or father's brother.
My uncle *came over for dinner.*

under *preposition* Under means directly below; beneath.
Come under *the umbrella so you won't get wet.*

unhappy *adjective* Unhappy means sad.
Sue was unhappy *because she was sick.*

uniform *noun* A uniform is a set of clothing that people wear to show that they belong to a certain group.
The police officer had a blue uniform.

unite *verb* To unite is to bring or come together.
The whole town united *to root for their team.*

unkind *adjective* Unkind means cruel or not nice.
She was unkind *to the people on the bus.*

untie *verb* To untie is too loosen; undo.
Can you untie *this knot?*

until *conjunction* Until means up to a certain time.
We slept until *ten o'clock!*

upside-down *adverb* Upside-down means the bottom is on the top and the top is on the bottom.
The monkey was hanging upside-down *from the tree.*

urban *adjective* Urban means in or related to a city.
I think urban *life is exciting!*

utter *verb* To utter is to make a sound or say something.
Do not utter *a sound.*

Can you write a sentence using a word from this page?

_____

_____

_____

vacant *adjective* Vacant means empty.
The old house was vacant.

vacuum cleaner *noun* A vacuum cleaner is a machine that picks up the dirt from carpets and rugs.
Plug the vacuum cleaner *into the wall.*

valentine *noun* A valentine is a card that you send to someone you like on February 14.
I need to make a valentine *for my mother.*

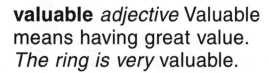

valuable *adjective* Valuable means having great value.
The ring is very valuable.

van *noun* A van is a large vehicle with space for a lot of people or things.
The van *can carry eight passengers.*

vanish *verb* To vanish is to disappear.
The magician made the handkerchief vanish.

vegetable *noun* A vegetable is an edible plant.
Vegetables are very good for you.

very *adverb* Very means extremely.
Aaron likes cars very *much.*

vest *noun* A vest is a jacket or sweater without sleeves.
She has a gray vest.

vigorously *adverb* Vigorously means with strength and energy.
He shook hands vigorously.

vine *noun* A vine is a climbing plant.
The vine *wrapped around the pole.*

violin *noun* A violin is a musical instrument with four strings that is played with a bow.
Erica plays the violin.

visit *verb* To visit is to go to see someone.
I went to visit *my grandmother on Sunday.*

Can you write a sentence using a word from this page?

_____

_____

_____

Ww

wagon *noun* A wagon is a cart used to carry people or things.
The wagon *carried the people to town.*

wallet *noun* A wallet is a small flat case used for carrying money or cards.
I put my money in my wallet.

wander *verb* To wander is to move from place to place without any direction.
We wandered *through the field looking for flowers.*

warn *verb* To warn is to tell in advance about something bad that might happen.
I must warn *Tim about the bee's nest in the backyard.*

watch *noun* A watch is a small clock worn on the wrist.
I left my watch *on the nightstand.*

weak *adjective* Weak means lacking strength or power.
She felt weak *after her operation.*

wearily *adverb* Wearily means in a tired way.
We went wearily *home from the soccer match.*

web *noun* A web is a net that a spider makes to catch insects
The spider caught a fly in its web.

weep *verb* To weep is to cry.
Linda will weep *through this movie.*

wheel *noun* A wheel is a round object with flat sides that rolls.
A tricycle has three wheels.

wicked *adjective* Wicked means very bad or evil.
The wicked *witch in the story frightened us.*

with *preposition* With refers to nouns grouped together.
I went to the dance with *Frank.*

worm *noun* A worm is a small legless creature that lives in the dirt.
The worm *was hidden under the dirt.*

wow *interjection* Wow is an exclamation of surprise.
Wow! *That is a fabulous outfit.*

Can you write a sentence using a word from this page?

_____

_____

_____

Xx

Xanadu *noun* Xanadu is an imaginary place of fantastic beauty. *Samuel T. Coleridge wrote a poem about* Xanadu.

x-ray *noun* An x-ray is a picture that shows the inside of the body. *The doctor took an* x-ray *of my foot.*

xylophone *noun* A xylophone is a musical instrument made of different-sized metal or wooden bars that are tapped with a small hammer. *My brother has a toy* xylophone.

There are not many other words that begin with this letter. There are many words, however, that end with the letter X or have the letter X in them. On the lines at right, make a list of words that contain or end with the letter X.

(Here is a hint. Many words begin with the letters ex—excellent.)

Yy

yacht *noun* A yacht is a large boat used for pleasure.
We were invited to go sailing on Ken's yacht.

yak *noun* A yak is a wild ox with long hair. *We saw a yak in the zoo.*

yam *noun* Yam is another name for a sweet potato.
I ate a slice of turkey and a yam for dinner.

yard *noun* A yard is a piece of land near a building.
The dog is out in the yard.

yarn *noun* Yarn is a kind of string made from wool, cotton or other materials.
Gina needs green yarn to finish knitting her scarf.

yawn *verb* To yawn is to open your mouth involuntarily to breath in, often when you are tired.
It is polite to cover your mouth when you yawn.

year *noun* A year is 365 days; the time it takes the earth to revolve around the sun.
I will go to third grade in a year.

yell *verb* To yell is to shout or call out loudly.
It upsets me when you yell.

yet *conjunction* Yet means up to the present time.
We haven't had lunch yet.

yikes *interjection* Yikes is an exclamation of surprise or alarm.
Yikes! *I didn't see you sitting there.*

yogurt *noun* Yogurt is a thick, soft food made from milk.
What flavor of yogurt *would you like to have?*

yo-yo *noun* A yo-yo is a round toy that goes up and down on a string.
My favorite yo-yo is green.

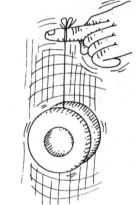

yuck *interjection* Yuck is an exclamation of disgust or dislike.
Yuck! *I just stepped in mud.*

Can you write a sentence using a word from this page?

_____

_____

_____

Zz

zebra *noun* A zebra is a black and white striped animal that looks like a horse.
I saw a herd of zebras *at the zoo.*

zeppelin *noun* A zeppelin is a large airship filled with a gas lighter than air.
We saw a zeppelin *high up in the sky.*

zero *noun* Zero is a number that equals nothing.
The score was Tigers three, Bears zero.

zinc *noun* Zinc is a hard, bluish white metal.
Batteries have zinc *in them.*

zingy *adjective* Zingy means sharply flavored; tangy.
This lemonade is zingy!

zinnia *noun* A zinnia is a type of brightly colored flower.
We have many zinnias *in our garden.*

zipper *noun* A zipper is a device for fastening and unfastening clothing.
I need to fix the zipper *on my jacket.*

zither *noun* A zither is a stringed instrument played with the fingers.
She played a song on the zither.

zodiac *noun* The zodiac is a section of the sky including the paths of all the planets.
There are twelve signs in the zodiac.

zombie *noun* In folklore, a zombie is a dead body that has been brought back to life.
The people screamed when they saw the zombie.

zoo *noun* A zoo is a place where animals are kept so that people can look at them.
We saw the gorillas at the zoo.

zoom *verb* To zoom is to move very quickly.
The car zoomed *past us.*

zucchini *noun* Zucchini is a type of oblong green squash.
I like fried zucchini.

Name It
Play this game with a partner. Think of a word. Try to describe what the word means without saying the word. Your partner must try to guess the word from your definition.

Name It Again
Ask a friend or parent to play this game. Think of a word. Think of another word that means the same thing. Name the word. The other player must name a word that means the same thing. For example: beautiful and gorgeous, sad and unhappy, pal and friend.

Words and Letters
Pick a letter. Write it down. Then write as many words as you can think of that begin with that letter. Try the letter b. Here are a few example words: ball, bat, balloon, bingo, boring, beetle, bus, and so on. You can use pages 225 and 226 for this game.

Letter to Letter
Try this with a friend. Pick a category, animals for example. One player names an animal such as a horse. The next player must think of another animal whose name begins with the letter that the first animal's name ended with like elephant. The game continues as players take turns naming animals (tiger, rhinoceros, seal, leopard, etc.). When you get stumped, try a new subject.

PRACTICE PAGE

PRACTICE PAGE

WRITING

A **paragraph** is a group of sentences that tell about one main idea.
A **narrative** paragraph tells about something someone did.

- Choose a topic.
- Write a main-idea sentence about it.
- Write detail sentences about it.

> I like to swim. I learned to swim when I was just two years old. Last summer I won a medal. Maybe next year I'll win one, too!

Now write about something you did.
Draw a picture to go with it.

_____

_____

_____

_____

_____

_____

_____

_____

Skills: Writing a narrative paragraph

WRITING

Look at these zoo animals. Think of what you already know about animals that live in the zoo. Now write a **paragraph** about zoo animals.

_____

_____

_____

_____

Skills: Observing and using prior knowledge to write a paragraph

WRITING

A **story** needs a beginning, middle, and end. Write **B** for the beginning, **M** for the middle and **E** for the end of this familiar tale.

_____ The Gingerbread Boy ran away from the old woman, the old man, and the cow.

_____ One day an old woman made a boy-shaped gingerbread cookie.

_____ The fox ate the Gingerbread Boy.

Now think about the story of the Gingerbread Boy. Write a different **ending** for the story!

_____

_____

_____

_____

_____

_____

_____

Skills: Writing a story ending

WRITING

Look at the picture. Think about what is going on. Then write a **story** about it. It helps to write down your ideas first.

What will you name the characters in your story? _____

_____

How will the story begin? _____

_____

How will the story end? _____

_____

Now write your story. _____

_____

_____

_____

_____

_____

_____

Skills: Writing a story

WRITING

Use **sensory** words when you describe things. Pick words that help others 'see,' 'hear,' 'taste,' 'smell,' and 'feel' what you do.
Read these descriptions.
Which one helps you know how the writer feels?

"I went back to Grandpa's farm. I used to live there. Grandpa has cows and horses. The farm is nice."

"I could taste the dust as I walked up the long farm road. Then I saw the old red barn. I heard the cows mooing. I smelled hot apple pie. Then I saw Grandpa running to me. It was good to be home!"

Now write a paragraph to describe a person, place, or thing. Use **sensory** words.

_____

_____

_____

_____

_____

_____

Skills: Writing a descriptive paragraph

WRITING

Poems tell about feelings. Some poems rhyme. But some do not.

The flowers in my garden
Are ready now to bloom.
I think I'll go and pick a few
And put them in my room.

Flowers stand tall
And watch the
    small ants
As they crawl by.

Be a poet. Look at the flowers. Write your feelings.

_____

_____

_____

_____

_____

_____

Skills: Writing poetry

WRITING

Poems tell about feelings. Remember, your poem may rhyme or not. It's your choice.

> Little furry kitten, as soft as can be,
> Please come home and live with me.

Here's one way to write a poem:

Animals	Line 1: One word (your subject)
Soft and furry	Line 2: Two descriptive words
Jump, tumble, purr	Line 3: Three action words
Kittens	Line 4: One word

Try writing a poem using the formula above.

_____

_____

_____

_____

Skills: Writing poetry

WRITING

A **journal** is like a diary. In it you write your thoughts and feelings about what you see and do. Later you can go back and read what happened in your past! And no one else can read your journal unless you say so.

Many people write in their journals every day.
Did you see or do anything interesting today?
Did anything funny happen?
Write a journal entry about your day.

_____

_____

_____

_____

_____

_____

_____

_____

Skills: Writing a journal entry

WRITING

When you write a **book report**, you tell:

- the name of the book
- the name of the author
- what the book is about
- whether you liked the book
- why you did or didn't like it.

Now, write a **book report** about THIS book!

The name of this book is: _____

_____

This book is written by (educational consultant): _____

_____

The book is about: _____

_____

I **did**
  didn't like the book because: _____

_____

_____

_____

_____

Skills: Writing a book report

WRITING

A letter has four important parts.
Read this letter to find out what each part tells.

6455 Spring Mill Road
Indianapolis, Indiana }----------**Heading**
January 1, 2000

Dear Grandma, }----------**Greeting**

    Happy New Year! I wish you could be here
for my birthday next week. Please try to come. }----------**Body**
I miss you a whole lot.

        Your grandson, }----------**Closing**
        Roger

Now **you** write a friendly letter to someone.

_____

_____ } **Heading**

_____

_____ } **Greeting**

_____

_____ } **Body**

_____

_____ } **Closing**

_____

Skills: Writing a friendly letter

PRACTICE PAGE

THINKING SKILLS

You need to **infer** what word a bunch of scrambled letters creates. It helps if you know the subject. All these scrambled words are things you've read and done in this book. Use the word box if you need help.

fractions	reading	multiply
math	phonics	addition
spelling	writing	sentences

DEARIGN _____

THAM _____

DIOATDIN _____

ARCOTFINS _____

PINGSELL _____

GRINWIT _____

LUTYMLIP _____

COSPNIH _____

TENNESSEC _____

Skills: Making inferences

THINKING SKILLS

A **rebus** is a puzzle that mixes picture and letter clues. Write what each rebus below spells out.

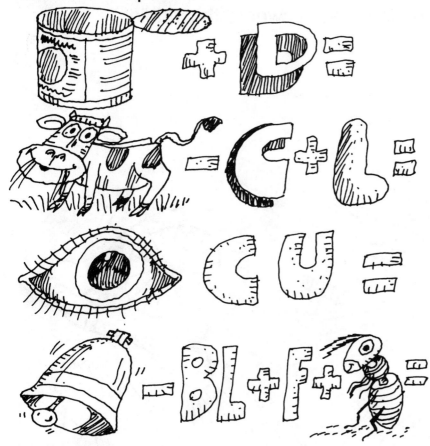

Next, draw a rebus to spell out this sentence: *I can hear my heart!*

_____

_____

Now, make up your own rebus! Write it in words. Then use pictures and letters to spell it out.

_____

_____

_____

_____

Skills: Making inferences

THINKING SKILLS

A code is a puzzle that uses pictures, letters, or numbers to stand for the letters in words.

Use the code key to help you decode the answer to this riddle:

Why can't a bicycle stand up by itself?

A	D	E	I	O	R	S	T	U	2
✛	■	★	♥	▲	●	◆	✳	✿	▼

♥ ✳   ♥ ◆   ✳ ▲ ▲ (▼)   ✳ ♥ ● ★ ■

__ __   __ __   __ __ __ (__)   __ __ __ __ __ __!

Skills: Making inferences

THINKING SKILLS

You can put facts together to **draw a conclusion**, or decide about things. Read each description below. Then actually **draw** your conclusion about what each thing is.

I have lots of teeth but I don't bite. However, I do nibble at the tangles you get in your hair! What am I?	I hang with a bunch in the warm sun. I'm yellow, good to eat, and have lots of a-PEEL! What am I?
I have a head but can't talk. I have feet but can't walk. You make me up, but I'm real. At night you lie down on me. What am I?	Look for me where people eat. I'm metal or plastic. I'm no help when you eat cereal, but I am when you eat spaghetti! What am I?

Skills: Drawing conclusions/inference

THINKING SKILLS

Read the sign. Then answer the questions.

What days will the fair be held? _____

What time is the fair? _____

What can people do at the fair? _____

What will the school do with the money they make? _____

_____

Do you think many people will come? _____

Why or why not? _____

_____

Skills: Drawing conclusions

THINKING SKILLS

Sometimes you have enough facts to **draw a conclusion**. But sometimes you don't. Read each example below. Circle the correct answer.

Everyone in my class came to my party. Jennifer is in my class. Did Jennifer come to my party?

      Yes   **No**   **You Can't Tell**

Marcie must be home by 8:00 p.m. on school nights. Monday she wants to go to a movie, but it ends at 9:30 p.m. Will Marcie go to the movie?

      Yes   **No**   **You Can't Tell**

My friend Jodi moved to Springfield. There's a Springfield in Massachusetts. Did Jodi move to Massachusetts?

      Yes   **No**   **You Can't Tell**

A person can get a driver's license after age 16. Ralph is 14 years old. Can he legally drive a car?

      Yes   **No**   **You Can't Tell**

The train from New York had 100 people on board. The train made two stops, but none of the 100 people got off. Are there still 100 on the train?

      Yes   **No**   **You Can't Tell**

Skills: Drawing conclusions/making judgments

THINKING SKILLS

Read about the children. Then look at each picture clue.
Write the answer in the crossword puzzle.

James has freckles. Jed does not. Addy has pigtails. Leda has curly hair.
Sammy has freckles and no front tooth. May has bangs. Amy and Lulu are
twins. Buddy has a striped shirt.

ACROSS

1.

5.

6.

7.

DOWN

1.

2.

3.

4.

5.

Skills: Drawing conclusions

THINKING SKILLS

An **analogy** lets you compare sets of things that are related in the same way. You know that a puppy is a young dog and a duckling is a young duck. So in an analogy you would say **puppy** is to **dog** as **duckling** is to **duck**.

> You can use : as a symbol for the words **is to** and **=** as a symbol for **as**, so…
>
> puppy : dog = duckling : duck

Think about what the first two words have in common. Then circle the picture that completes the analogy.

sneaker : foot = hat :

bear : cub = horse :

wing : airplane = sail :

ears : stereo = eyes :

skyscraper : buildings = pine :

rug : floor = curtain :

water : swim = snow :

Skills: Making analogies

THINKING SKILLS

Draw what should come next in each analogy.

Skills: Creating analogies

THINKING SKILLS

Analogies can be made using any relationship, or thing that two sets have in common. Read each analogy. Circle the word that tells what relationship was used.

mouse : squeak = duck : quack

age   sound   color

bowl : fish = hive : bees

shape   home   amount

ore : store = one : stone

letters   rocks   height

skin : human = feathers : bird

shape   weight   covering

flour : bread = milk : pudding

weight   color   ingredients

Now write the end to each of these analogies.

art : museum = books : _____

soft : loud = whisper : _____

dress : silk = table : _____

horn : toot = drum : _____

tulip : plant = orange : _____

Skills: Creating analogies

THINKING SKILLS

Be a detective. Find the stolen treasure.
Read the note the thieves dropped by mistake.
Draw a path on the map.
Make an **X** where the treasure is buried!

> Go out the back door of the house. Walk south to the big rock. Turn and go east to the wooden gate. Now go north past the tall trees. Turn and go west around the lake. The treasure is under the second park bench.

Skills: Sequencing; Map reading

THINKING SKILLS

Read each list. All the things belong to a group, or **category**. Add one more item to each list. Then write each group's classification. Use the word box to help you. The first one has been done for you.

animals	careers	books	machines
	countries	plants	sounds

carpenter	washer	Mexico	boom
actor	computer	England	bang
teacher	bulldozer	Italy	crash
writer	car	Japan	POW!
doctor			

| careers | | | |

tree	*Green Eggs and Ham*		lion
rose	*Curious George*		koala
bush	*Winnie the Pooh*		snake
grass	*The Tale of*		yak
	Peter Rabbit		

Now create your own list for the category **sports**.

_____

_____

_____

_____

Skills: Classification

249

THINKING SKILLS

Look at the two pictures. They look somewhat alike...but a few things are different. Find and circle the 10 differences between the two pictures.

Skills: Visual discrimination

THINKING SKILLS

Have you ever heard someone say:

- "It's much colder than it was last winter."
- "I'm as tall as my cousin Pat."
- "You are two years older than I am."
- "I did better on the last spelling test."
- "Hey, I have a bike just like yours!"

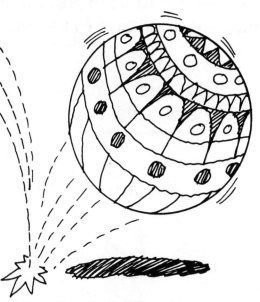

When we think of how two things are alike, we **compare** them.
When we think of how two things are different, we **contrast** them.
Read each feature. Does it apply to a ball? An orange?
Make an **X** in the column where it is true.

Feature	Ball	Orange
Round		
Comes in many colors		
Squeeze juice from it		
Bounces		
Rolls		
Good to eat		
Stays usable for years		
Sweet to eat		
Made of rubber		
Can use half of it at a time		

Skills: Comparing and contrasting

THINKING SKILLS

Compare and **contrast** the things in the puzzles below.
How are they alike? How are they different?

Puzzle Parts

Circle the puzzle that has the **most** parts. Underline the puzzle that has the **fewest** parts.

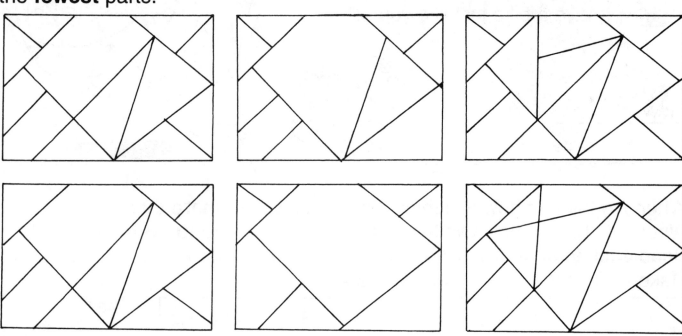

Pastry Pair

Circle the two cakes that are exactly alike. Underline the look-alike pies.

Skills: Comparing and contrasting

THINKING SKILLS

You can make a chart to show comparisons. Look at the animal chart.
Some information is given for each animal.
Finish the chart by writing the same kind of information for the other animals.

Cow	Sheep	Chicken
says "moo"		
	soft, wooly	
		lives on farms
gives milk		
	has four legs	
		baby called chick

Skills: Comparing and contrasting

THINKING SKILLS

What's going on here? Circle each thing in the picture that's wrong.

Skills: Visual discrimination; Logic; Inference

THINKING SKILLS

A **pattern** is something repeating in the same order.
You see patterns all around you on wallpaper, clothing, animal coverings, flowers, and leaves. The year follows a pattern, too, from spring to summer to fall to winter every year!

Look at the pattern in each row. Circle the object that should come next in the pattern.

Skills: Patterning

THINKING SKILLS

Draw what should come next in each pattern.

Skills: Patterning

THINKING SKILLS

Do you know how to give directions? Then you know how important it is to give directions in order, or **step-by-step sequence**.
After all, you can't eat a cake before you bake it! You can't fly a kite until you go out in the wind.

The step-by-step directions below got all mixed up. Number the directions in the right order (**1**, **2**, **3**, and so on).

Make a Sandwich

_____ Cut the sandwich in half.

_____ Spread peanut butter on one slice.

_____ Put the two slices of bread together.

_____ Get two slices of bread, a knife, and jars of peanut butter and jelly.

_____ Spread jelly on the other slice.

_____ Clean up and put things away.

_____ Put bread on a plate.

Skills: Sequencing; Problem solving

THINKING SKILLS

Michael wanted to play kickball with his friends.
He made this list about how to get the game started.

> 1. Pick teams.
> 2. Get a kickball.
> 3. Play kickball game.
> 4. Choose who goes first.

Michael's friends came over. They tried to follow his directions for starting a game. Suddenly, Sandy said, "These steps are in the wrong order!" She crossed out the numbers. She renumbered the steps to make sense. Then the kids played kickball!

Number the steps on Michael's list the way you think Sandy did.

> ___ Pick teams.
>
> ___ Get a kickball.
>
> ___ Play kickball game.
>
> ___ Choose who goes first.

Skills: Sequencing

THINKING SKILLS

A **flowchart** shows step-by-step directions. Shapes make it easy to read a flowchart.

- Oval ⬭ is for **Start** or **Stop**.

- Rectangle ▭ is for information about a step.

- Diamond is for questions. Answer **yes** or **no**.

- Arrow ⟶ points from one step to another.

Read this flowchart. What does it tell you how to do?

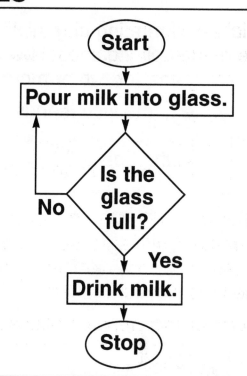

Now make a flowchart for how to mail a letter using these steps.

Start
Put letter in envelope.
Did you seal the envelope?
Seal the envelope.
Put on postage stamp.
Drop letter in mailbox.
Stop

Skills: Sequencing

THINKING SKILLS

You need reading and thinking skills when you play games. Here's a board game for two or more people.

Play the game with friends. Take turns. Use buttons as markers to move on the board.

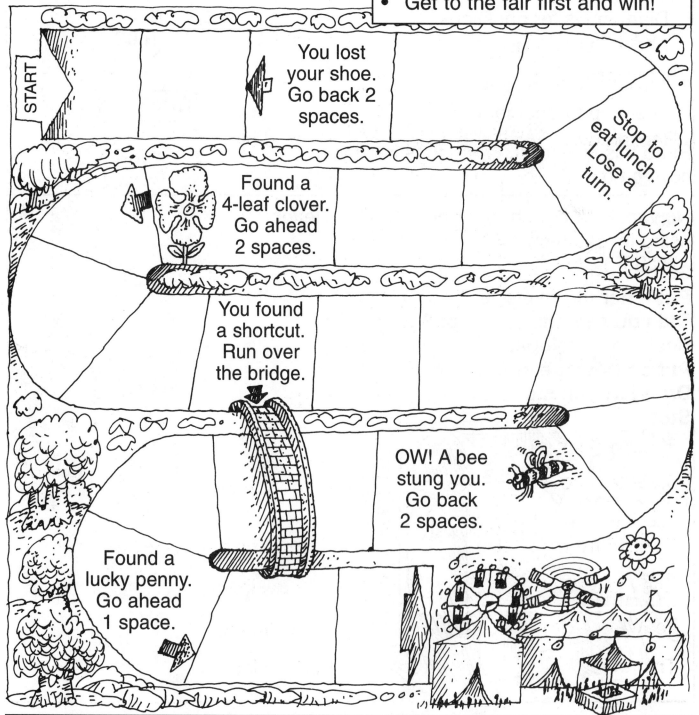

Skills: Sequencing; Problem solving; Following directions

THINKING SKILLS

Things can be **ranked**, or put in order, by something they have in common. Read each list, then circle the words that tell how the things are ranked.

1. Grandpa	83 years
2. Dad	43
3. Mom	37
4. Jasper	7
5. Melissa	1

Ranked by:

height

age

weight

1. Ralph	142 pounds
2. Dan	121
3. Ken	97
4. Ruth	86
5. Tessa	51

Ranked by:

height

age

weight

1. Eat an apple

2. Frost a cake

3. Read a recipe

4. Bake a pie

5. Write a cookbook

Ranked from:

Easy to difficult

Young to old

Thin to fat

1. 6:00 a.m.

2. 10:00 a.m.

3. Noon

4. 6:00 p.m.

5. 11:00 p.m.

Ranked from:

Fast to slow

Old to young

Early to late

Skills: Classifying; Sequencing

THINKING SKILLS

Start at **START** and go where the arrows go. If there's no arrow, keep going in the same direction. Write each letter on the lines. The letters spell words and the words form a secret message.

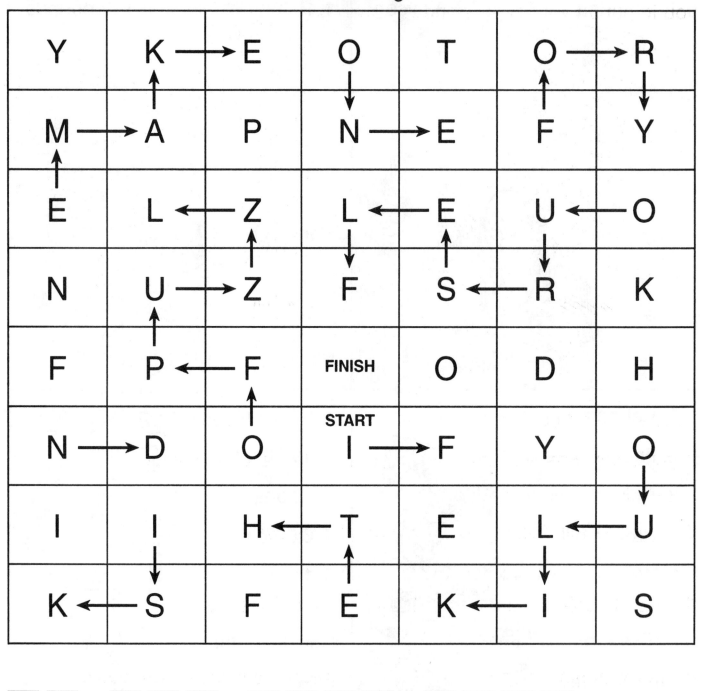

_ _   _ _   _ _ _ _   _ _ _

_ _ _ _   _ _   _ _ _ _ _ _ ,   _ _ _ _

_ _ _   _ _ _   _ _ _ _ _ _

Skills: Sequencing; Inference

THINKING SKILLS

An **if...then** sentence tells you that one thing must be true before another thing can happen. Suppose your mom says, "**If** you finish your homework, **then** you can go in-line skating." You finish your homework. Is it okay for you to put on your skates and roll away?

If...then statements are true only if they make sense and are sure to happen. Read each example below. Circle your answers.

If yesterday was Monday, **then** tomorrow will be Wednesday.

    True   **Not certain**

If it doesn't rain today, **then** it will rain tomorrow.

    True   **Not certain**

If I like chocolate ice cream, **then** my mother likes it too.

    True   **Not certain**

If the ice cream shop is closed, **then** you can't buy ice cream there.

    True   **Not certain**

If the teacher gives a test, **then** everyone will pass it.

    True   **Not certain**

Skills: If...then logic

THINKING SKILLS

Sometimes an **if...then** sentence has the word **and** or **or**. Mom says, "**If** Mrs. Smith comes over **and** asks for my blow dryer, **then** give it to her." Mrs. Smith comes over but says she'll come back later. Should you give her the hair dryer? Why or why not?

Read each example below. Watch for the **and** or **or**. Circle your answers.

"**If** it's nice on Tuesday **and** I can get off work, **then** I'll be at the game," Bill said. Bill had to work Tuesday. Did he go to the game?

   Yes   **No**

"**If** you were absent yesterday **or** missed the spelling test last week, **then** please raise your hand," said the teacher. You've been in school all week. You took the test last week. Should you raise your hand?

   Yes   **No**

If your birthday was on December 31 this year **and** you were 7 years old, **then** next year on December 31 you'll be 8 years old.

   Yes   **No**

Skills: If...then logic

THINKING SKILLS

There are four kinds of kites in the sky. Look closely at the picture. Then follow the instructions.

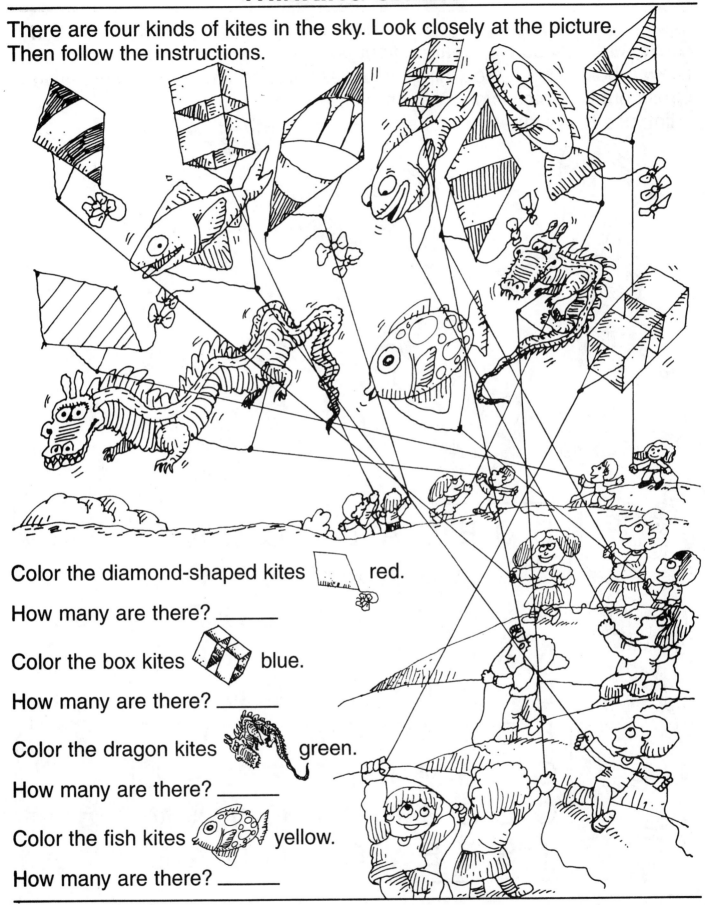

Color the diamond-shaped kites red.

How many are there? _____

Color the box kites blue.

How many are there? _____

Color the dragon kites green.

How many are there? _____

Color the fish kites yellow.

How many are there? _____

Skills: Classifying; Counting

THINKING SKILLS

Look at the letter grid.
Circle three things you wear on your feet.
Draw a box around three things you wear around your neck.
Cross out two things you wear on your hands.
(Hint: use the pictures as clues.)

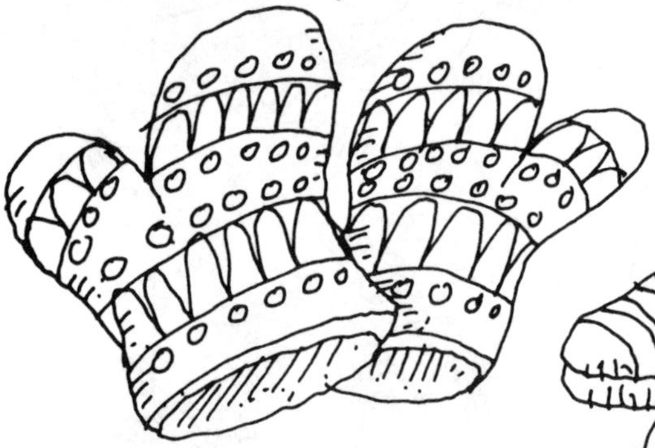

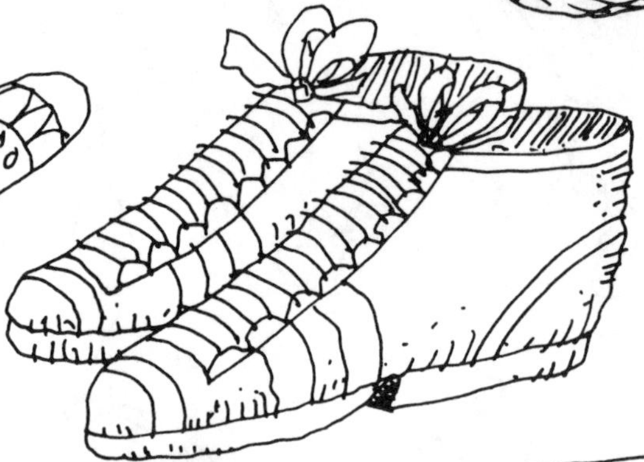

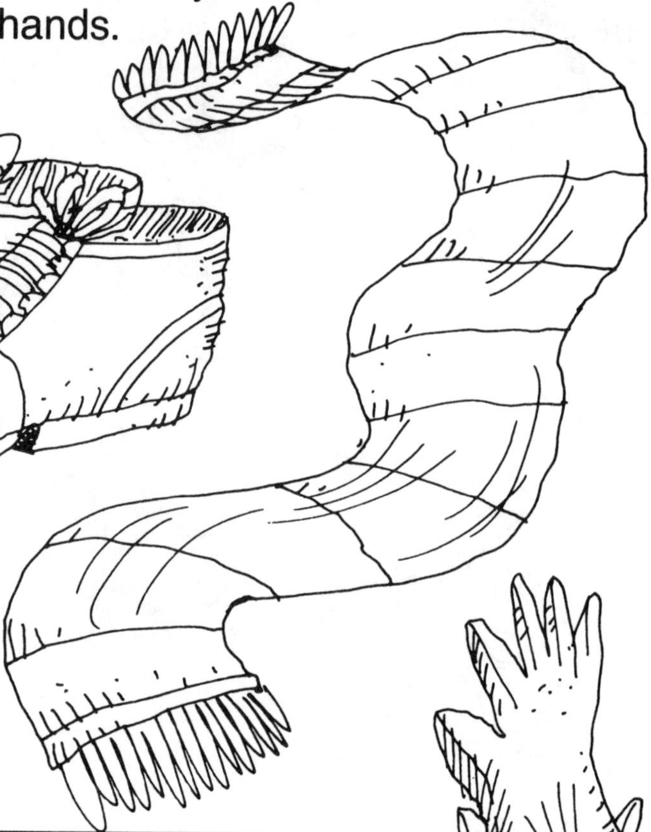

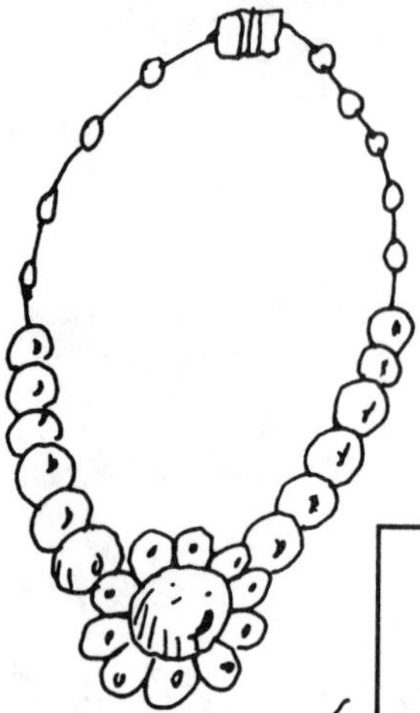

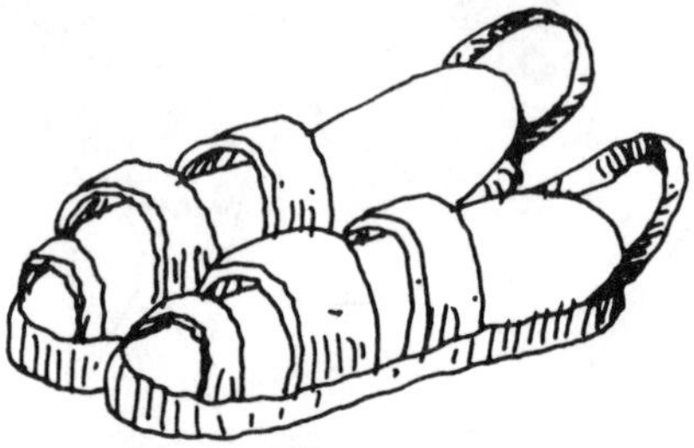

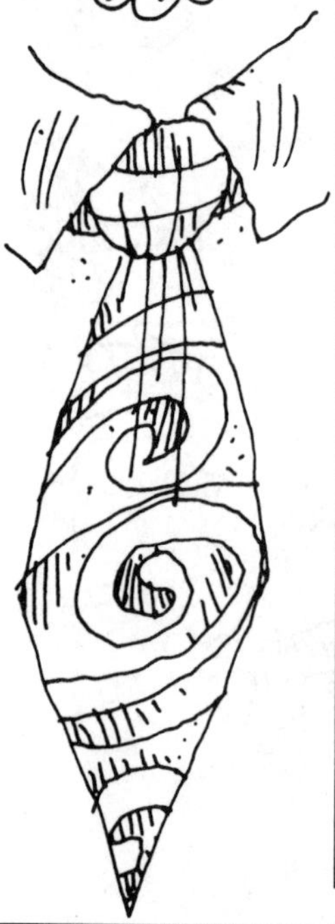

```
B O E C A L K C E N Q
S B D B N G I K M O Z
A S H O E S H E O F L
N A B O C A R F A R F
D N X T K Y L E N A M
F D A S T C M I T C K
O A G M I T T E N S I
O L C S E G L O V X M
T S S E V O L G Q A E
```

Skills: Classifying

266

THINKING SKILLS

What do you think of when you hear the word **music**?
Maybe you think of different kinds of music, like **rock**, **country**, or **jazz**.
Or maybe you think of people and things in music, like **singer**, **violin**,
melody, or **concert**.
Each word you think of may make you think of two or three more words.
Look at the filled-in chart for the word **baseball**.

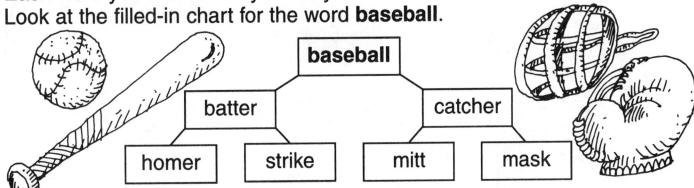

	baseball	
batter		catcher
homer	strike	mitt	mask

Now fill in your own chart by thinking of the word **food**.

food

Skills: Making inferences; Word association

Who's Who?

You're going to meet your cousin Homer at the train station.
But you've never seen Homer.
When you get to the station you see five kids who might be Homer.
Read each clue, then circle the real cousin Homer.

- His shoelaces are untied.
- He is not wearing sunglasses.
- He's wearing his favorite baseball cap.
- He's shorter than the boy on his right.

Skills: Deduction; Drawing conclusions

THINKING SKILLS

Alex, Claire, Jenny, and Patrick brought things to the bake sale. But who baked what? Read the clues below.

Make ✓ for **yes** or O for **no** to discover which goodies each person baked.

- The kid who baked muffins sits next to Alex in math.
  (Hint: Alex is not the muffin maker.)

- Jenny lives next door to the boy who baked cookies.

- The girl who baked a pie bought a piece of Patrick's cake.

- The muffins are on the same table as the food that Claire baked.

	Cake	Cookie	Muffin	Pie
Alex				
Claire				
Jenny				
Patrick				

Skills: Deduction

THINKING SKILLS

Andy, Erin, Maggie, and Stuart have pets. But what kind? Read the clues. Make ✓ for **yes** or **O** for **no** to discover what kind of pet each kid has.

- Erin's pet gets scared when the cat meows.
  (Hint: Erin's pet isn't a cat!)

- The girl with the cat doesn't like reptiles, but loves to play with Stuart's pet.

- Erin bought her pet at the same store that the dog came from.

- Andy lives next door to the boy with the hamster.

	Cat	Dog	Hamster	Lizard
Andy				
Erin				
Maggie				
Stuart				

Skills: Deduction

THINKING SKILLS

Write one of these numbers in each circle. Make each side of the triangle add up to 64. Do not repeat any number.

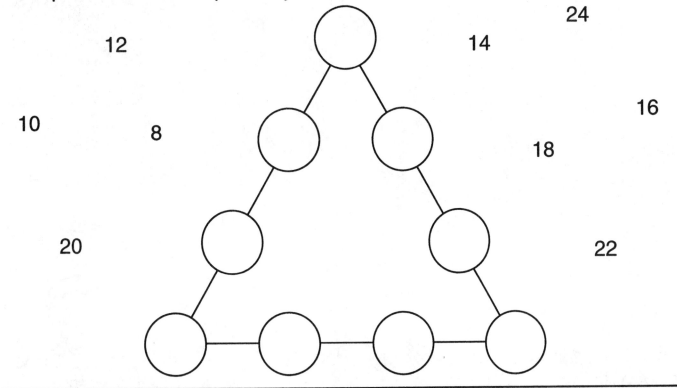

12   24   14   10   8   16   18   20   22

Write only **even** numbers from 2 to 18 in the circles so any three circles in a line have a sum of 30. Do not repeat any number.

THINKING SKILLS

Which path should the kids take to get to the water fountain?
Find the way and save the day!

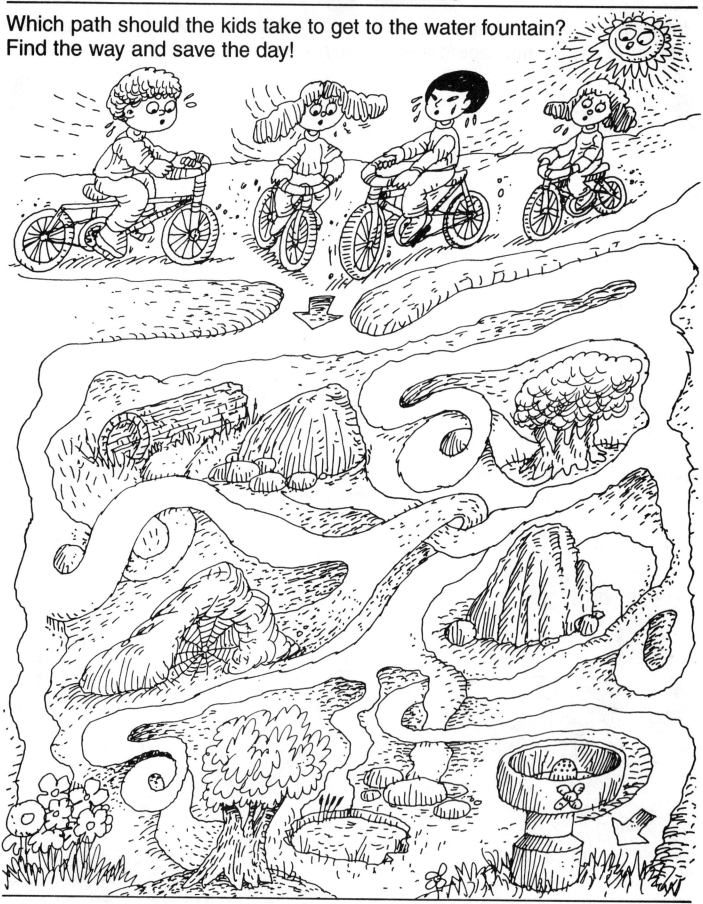

Skills: Visual discrimination

THINKING SKILLS

Help the bears choose which path to take to get to their den. They need to get inside before the snow gets too deep! Show the bears which path has ONLY words from this paragraph! It's the right path.

this get inside bears help sunshine go can

paragraph path snow deep bears before

right path den bears only go inside snow

Skills: Visual discrimination; Reading skills

THINKING SKILLS

Look at the map above. Follow the directions below.

- Exit the school onto Main Street.

- Go east to the corner and turn south onto Elm Street.

- Turn east onto Market Street by the newsstand.

- Go east 3 blocks to Flower Street.

- Go north on Flower and turn west onto Main Street.

- Go past the ice cream shop and stop in front of the blue house.

- Look across Main Street.
  What building do you see? _____

Skills: Tracking; Following map directions

THINKING SKILLS

Start with the letter **N** in the middle of the maze. Trace your way out of the maze without crossing any lines. Write the letters on your path on the lines under the puzzle. You'll find a special message just for you!

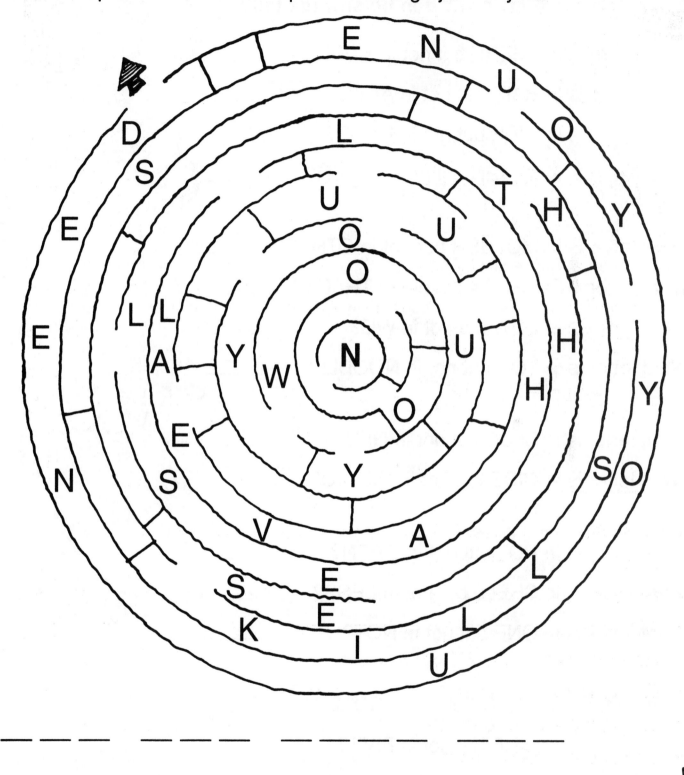

—— —— —— —— —— —— —— —— —— —— ——

—— —— —— —— —— —— —— ——!

Skills: Deduction; Making inferences; Visual discrimination

THINKING SKILLS

Write the correct letter on the line. Then read the letters from top to bottom. They form the answer to the riddle.

What did the bunny say when he saw his tail?

What letter is in THERE but not in HERE? _____

What letter is in HAIR but not in AIR? _____

What letter is in RIDE but not in DARE? _____

What letter is in SEVEN but not in EVEN? _____

What letter is in MOTHER but not in OTHER? _____

What letter is in TRUCK but not in TRACK? _____

What letter is in SEW but not in WE? _____

What letter is in TON but not in NOODLE? _____

What letter is in BLUE but not in GLUE? _____

What letter is in RIDE but not in RIDING? _____

What letter is in POT but not in OPEN? _____

What letter is in SHELL but not in LESS? _____

What letter is in ONE but not in NOT? _____

What letter is in READ but not in ROAD? _____

What letter is in FINE but not in FIVE? _____

What letter is in SHADE but not in ASHES? _____

Skills: Making inferences; Drawing conclusions

PRACTICE PAGE

PRACTICE PAGE

ANSWERS

Page 6

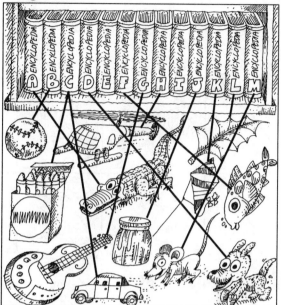

Page 7

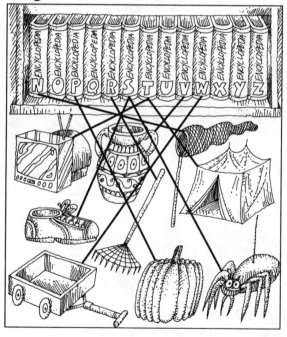

Page 8

Page 9

1. apple
2. boots
3. chair
4. jet
5. mitten
6. nine
7. pig
8. snake

Page 10

1. bird
2. cake
3. doll
4. fork

5. hand
6. log
7. ring
8. sun

ANSWERS

Page 11

1. bat	2. bring	3. bus
1. sand	2. ship	3. silly
1. water	2. will	3. wolf
1. fall	2. fox	3. funny
1. read	2. ride	3. roll

Page 12

C X

Page 13

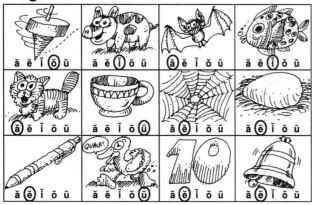

Page 14

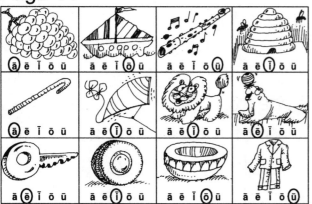

Page 15

Page 16

Page 17

I like to rake leaves.
We like to skate.
My bike has two wheels.
It is really neat to play the flute.

ANSWERS

Page 18

Is that a <u>snake</u> I see?

Don't you <u>like</u> pizza?

We planted some <u>seeds</u>.

Many fish live in the <u>ocean</u>.

Your little sister is <u>cute</u>!

Page 19

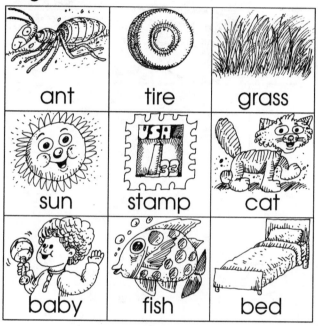

Page 20

Page 21

I wore a cap on my <u>head</u>.

I got a <u>book</u> from the library.

Rockets <u>launch</u> the space shuttle.

She wasn't in <u>school</u> today.

Page 22

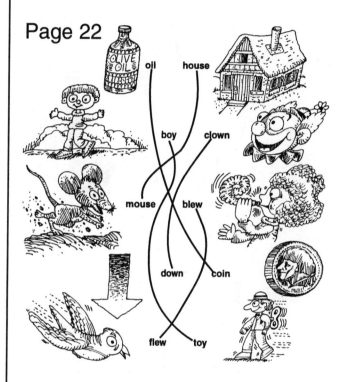

Page 23

I saw a funny <u>clown</u> at the circus.

We really <u>enjoy</u> playing at the park.

Plant seeds in the <u>soil</u>.

The elevator goes up and <u>down</u>.

ANSWERS

Page 24

Page 26

d	
k	
p	
n	
s	

Page 25

	b	j	(z)	r	d
	h	z	d	(m)	n
	(b)	k	g	c	r
	m	(c)	a	f	d
	n	u	(v)	t	s
	s	(h)	r	o	k

Page 27

	k	(g)	z	r	d
	h	z	(t)	m	n
	(b)	k	d	c	l
	m	v	(n)	f	d
	k	u	z	(p)	s
	s	(l)	r	o	n

ANSWERS

Page 28

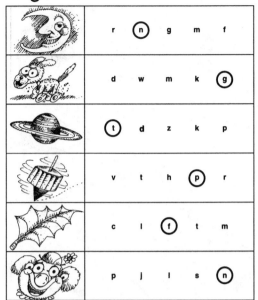

	r **n** g m f
	d w m k **g**
	t d z k p
	v t h **p** r
	c l **f** t m
	p j l s **n**

Page 29

<u>h</u>at	<u>p</u>ig	<u>s</u>un
<u>p</u>in	<u>f</u>an	m<u>a</u>sk
<u>bell</u>	hand	cup
<u>duck</u>	<u>c</u>a<u>t</u>	<u>s</u>aw

Page 30

Page 31

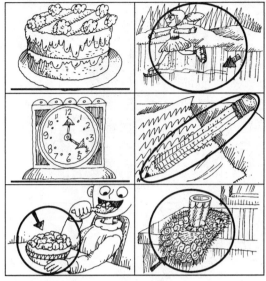

Page 32

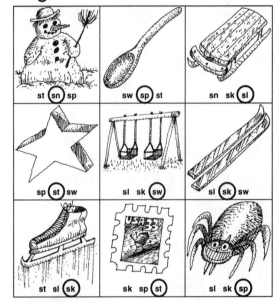

st **sn** sp	sw **sp** st	sn sk **sl**
sp **st** sw	sl sk **sw**	sl **sk** sw
st sl **sk**	sk sp **st**	sl sk **sp**

Page 33

fl cl **pl**	pl **cl** gl	gl bl **fl**
plant	cloud	flag
bl cl pl	fl **cl** gl	**cl** fl pl
block	clock	flute
bl **fl** gl	bl cl **gl**	**cl** pl fl
flower	globe	plane

283

ANSWERS

Page 34

trim (train) trip   dream drive (drum)   (broom) bright bridge

graph group (grapes)   from (frog) free   print price (prince)

drop (dress) drag   tray truck (tree)   break (bridge) brick

Page 35

sta(mp)   be(lt)   ma(sk)

ra(ft)   sku(nk)   fish ta(nk)

la(mp)   pla(nt)   de(sk)

Page 36

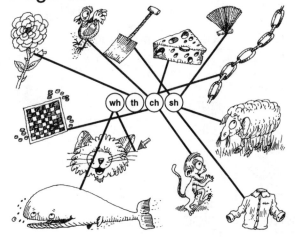

Page 37

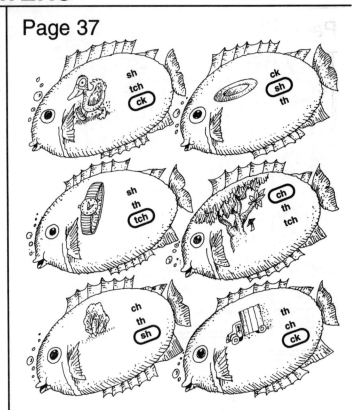

Page 38

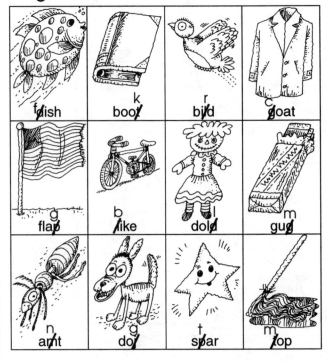

f(ish)   boo(k)   bi(rd)   (c)oat

fla(g)   (b)ike   dol(l)   gu(m)

a(n)t   do(g)   s(t)ar   (m)op

ANSWERS

Page 39

They name <u>animals</u>.

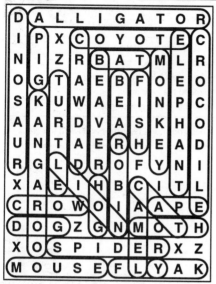

Page 40

Clothing	Fruit	Fruit
hat	orange	desk
dress	apple	chair
jeans	grapes	bed
boots	pineapple	sofa
coat	pear	lamp
shoes	banana	table

Page 41

Toys	People	Things to Read
doll	mother	newspaper
train	teacher	magazine
top	doctor	mail
kite	father	books
wagon	baby	
blocks		

Page 42

Cause	Effect
Read each problem. Make a ✓ in front of any likely cause.	Read each problem. Make a ✓ in front of any likely effect.
1. Andy doesn't have a dog because	1. We just moved to town, so I
✓ he likes cats better.	✓ go to a new school.
— he likes to watch TV.	— wear red shoes.
✓ he has an allergy.	✓ miss my old friends.
✓ his mother won't buy one.	✓ have a new house.
2. I'm going on the train because	2. We were hungry after school, so we
✓ my grandpa lives far away.	✓ fixed popcorn.
— I like to skate.	✓ had cookies and milk.
✓ I have a ticket.	— went to sleep.
— a bear is in the circus.	✓ asked mom for a snack.

Page 43

A bird popped the balloon.
A car ran over the balloon.
Racquel ate the balloon.

The dog drank the milk
The baby spilled her milk.
Mother dropped a glass.

It is Thursday.
Maria is going to the beach.
It is starting to rain.

The wind knocked over our castle.
A big wave hit our castle.
A big bad wolf blew over our castle.

Page 46

sad	silly
happy	
sleepy	(glad)

funny	(yell)
shout	
tall	slow

start	(quit)
stop	
loud	old

brave	fast
afraid	
like	(scared)

angry	(tired)
sleepy	
speedy	silly

ANSWERS

Page 47

behind   out
above
in   (below)

silly   (sad)
happy
funny   cheerful

over   near
down
close   (up)

young   (old)
new
last   now

evening   moon
night
noon   (day)

Page 48

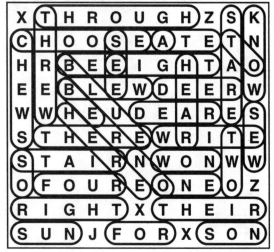

Page 49

2 Humpty Dumpty had a great fall.
1 Humpty Dumpty sat on a wall.
4 They couldn't put Humpty together again.
3 All the king's horses and men came to help.

4 The spider climbed the spout again.
1 The eensy-weensy spider went up the water spout.
3 Up came the sun and dried up all the rain.
2 Down came the rain and washed the spider out.

Page 50

Story Title	Jack and the Beanstalk	
Characters	Jack His mother	The golden goose The giant
Important Events	1. Mother sent Jack to sell the cow. 2. He traded her for magic beans. 3. The beans grew into a tall beanstalk. 4. Jack climbed the beanstalk. 5. Jack took the giant's golden goose.	
Ending	Jack chopped down the beanstalk and killed the giant.	

Page 55

(Oil spills can harm animals) Sometimes big ships spill oil into the ocean. Birds that swim in the water get oil in their feathers. They can't swim or fly. Some birds swallow the oil. Many birds die.

People want to help the birds. They try to clean off the oil. Some birds are saved.

Page 56

(We should respect our flag) It is a symbol of America. We stand when the flag goes by in a parade. Why? We show others that we respect our country. We say the *Pledge of Allegiance* to show our respect for our country, too. Do you know all the words to the *Pledge of Allegiance*? Do you know what the words mean?

FOR A CHALLENGE:
Can you name any other symbols of America? Try to list at least two more.

eagle   Star Spangled Banner

ANSWERS

Page 57

The story tells how a baby duck hatches from an egg.	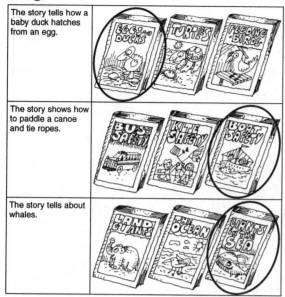
The story shows how to paddle a canoe and tie ropes.	
The story tells about whales.	

Page 58

a card (a red bow) a green bow

Mother's   Sam's   (Sabrina's)

a box (a hug)   a bow

bike   bear   jump rope   doll   ice skates
pair of boots (train) wooden puzzle

Page 59

1. What kind of pet does Juan have?
2. What kind of pet does Chris have?
3. What kind of pet does Pat have?
4. What kind of pet does Miss Andrews have?

Page 60

1. Earth is running out of space for _____.

    schools   animals   (trash)

2. Old paper, plastic, cans, and glass can be _____.

    eaten   (recycled)   written

3. Old glass can be used for repairing _____.

    (streets)   stockings   clocks

4. Look for recycled things when you _____.

    sleep   swim   (shop)

Page 61

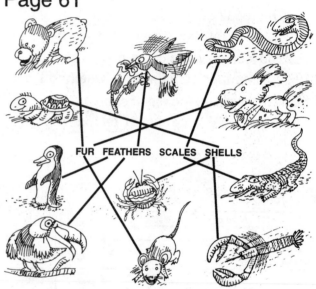

FUR   FEATHERS   SCALES   SHELLS

Page 62

<u>T</u> 1. Moles need the sense of touch to get around.
<u>T</u> 2. Butterflies taste with their feet.
<u>N</u> 3. Flies taste with their eyes.
<u>T</u> 4. Mice use whiskers to feel in the dark.

287

ANSWERS

Page 63

T 1. Dinosaurs once lived on earth.

T 2. Some birds are colorful.

N 3. Scientists are sure what colors dinosaurs were.

Page 64

2 Maria tried to turn on the _____.

    stove   computer   (TV)

1 The children ate _____ quickly.

    lunch   (breakfast)   dinner

5 The repair shop _____ the TV.

    broke   bought   (fixed)

4 The kids played a game and _____.

    napped   (painted)   watched TV

3 Mother called the repair shop on the _____

    TV   cooker   (telephone)

Page 65

Alike or Different?	Ginny	Mark
Is a second grader	X	X
Is in Miss Murray's class		X
Is in Mr. Howard's class	X	
Has music on Fridays	X	X
Likes gym best		X
Likes art class best	X	
Goes to the library on Tuesdays	X	
Goes to the library on Wednesdays		X
Has a best friend in Greenbay School	X	X

Page 66

1. Groundhogs live _____.

    in the ocean   **in caves**   (underground)

2. Groundhogs are covered with _____.

    scales   (fur)   feathers

3. Groundhogs are afraid of their _____.

    food   leaf   (shadows)

4. Groundhogs want _____ to come.

    (spring)   winter   turtles

5. Groundhogs sleep in the _____.

    rainbow   (dark)   water

Page 67

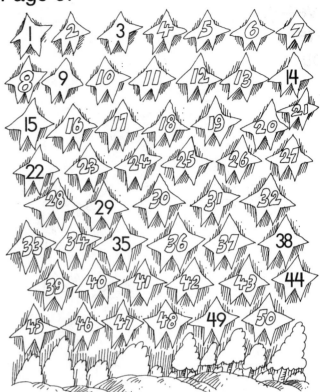

Page 68

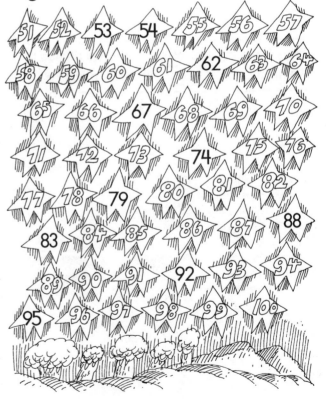

ANSWERS

Page 69

5	10	15	20
25	30	35	40
45	50	55	60
65	70	75	80
85	90	95	100

Page 71

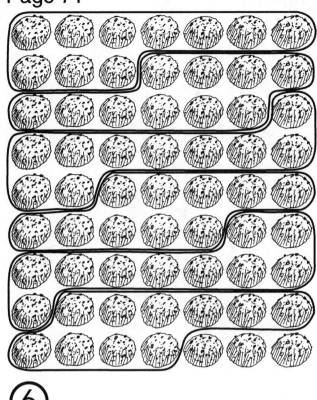

6

Page 70

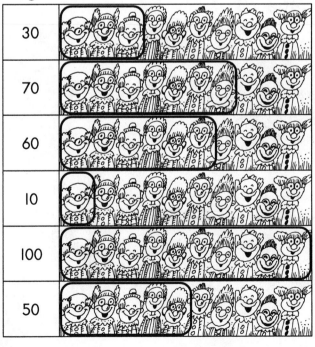

30	
70	
60	
10	
100	
50	

Page 72

ANSWERS

Page 73

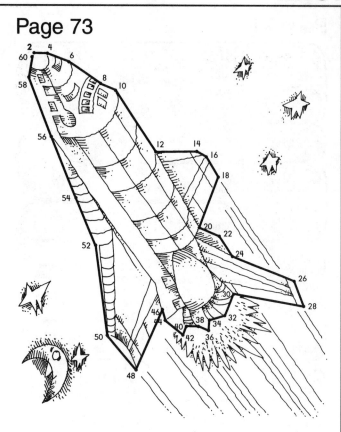

Page 75

Page 74

4	6	8	<u>10</u>	<u>12</u>
3	5	7	<u>9</u>	<u>11</u>
14	12	10	<u>8</u>	<u>6</u>
16	18	20	<u>22</u>	<u>24</u>
13	11	9	<u>7</u>	<u>5</u>
15	17	19	<u>21</u>	<u>23</u>

Page 76

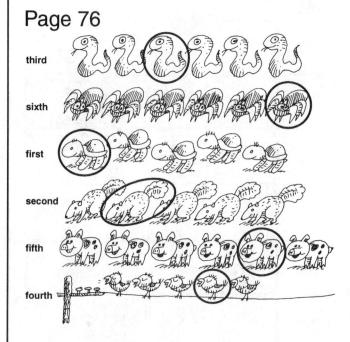

ANSWERS

Page 77

first	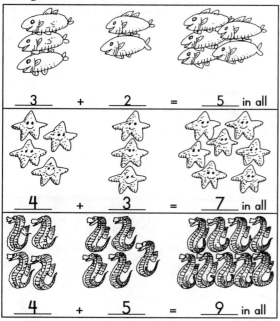
second	
third	
sixth	
fifth	
eighth	

Page 78

$$3 + 2 = 5 \text{ in all}$$

$$4 + 3 = 7 \text{ in all}$$

$$4 + 5 = 9 \text{ in all}$$

Page 79

$$2 + 2 = \underline{4} \qquad 2 + 3 = \underline{5}$$
$$3 + 5 = \underline{8} \qquad 6 + 4 = \underline{10}$$
$$7 + 1 = \underline{8} \qquad 5 + 9 = \underline{14}$$

$$\begin{array}{r} 3 \\ +4 \\ \hline 7 \end{array} \qquad \begin{array}{r} 8 \\ +5 \\ \hline 13 \end{array} \qquad \begin{array}{r} 10 \\ +6 \\ \hline 16 \end{array} \qquad \begin{array}{r} 15 \\ +2 \\ \hline 17 \end{array}$$

$$\begin{array}{r} 9 \\ +8 \\ \hline 17 \end{array} \qquad \begin{array}{r} 6 \\ +5 \\ \hline 11 \end{array} \qquad \begin{array}{r} 10 \\ +2 \\ \hline 12 \end{array} \qquad \begin{array}{r} 8 \\ +8 \\ \hline 16 \end{array}$$

Page 80

$$\begin{array}{r} 44 \\ +17 \\ \hline 61 \end{array} \quad \begin{array}{r} 56 \\ +28 \\ \hline 84 \end{array} \quad \begin{array}{r} 27 \\ +36 \\ \hline 63 \end{array} \quad \begin{array}{r} 31 \\ +39 \\ \hline 70 \end{array}$$

$$\begin{array}{r} 62 \\ +19 \\ \hline 81 \end{array} \quad \begin{array}{r} 16 \\ +38 \\ \hline 54 \end{array} \quad \begin{array}{r} 12 \\ +38 \\ \hline 50 \end{array} \quad \begin{array}{r} 45 \\ +29 \\ \hline 74 \end{array}$$

$$\begin{array}{r} 39 \\ +12 \\ \hline 51 \end{array} \quad \begin{array}{r} 22 \\ +59 \\ \hline 81 \end{array} \quad \begin{array}{r} 42 \\ +49 \\ \hline 91 \end{array} \quad \begin{array}{r} 17 \\ +38 \\ \hline 55 \end{array}$$

Page 81

$$\begin{array}{r} 16 \\ +13 \\ \hline \textcircled{28} \end{array} \quad \begin{array}{r} 32 \\ +32 \\ \hline 64 \end{array} \quad \begin{array}{r} 15 \\ +17 \\ \hline 32 \end{array} \quad \begin{array}{r} 22 \\ +18 \\ \hline 40 \end{array} \quad \begin{array}{r} 19 \\ +15 \\ \hline 34 \end{array}$$

$$\begin{array}{r} 29 \\ +13 \\ \hline \textcircled{47} \end{array} \quad \begin{array}{r} 32 \\ +17 \\ \hline 49 \end{array} \quad \begin{array}{r} 28 \\ +36 \\ \hline 64 \end{array} \quad \begin{array}{r} 14 \\ +63 \\ \hline \textcircled{75} \end{array} \quad \begin{array}{r} 11 \\ +86 \\ \hline 97 \end{array}$$

$$\begin{array}{r} 44 \\ +39 \\ \hline 83 \end{array} \quad \begin{array}{r} 50 \\ +18 \\ \hline \textcircled{69} \end{array} \quad \begin{array}{r} 46 \\ +53 \\ \hline 99 \end{array} \quad \begin{array}{r} 20 \\ +63 \\ \hline 83 \end{array} \quad \begin{array}{r} 55 \\ +16 \\ \hline 71 \end{array}$$

$$\begin{array}{r} 48 \\ +43 \\ \hline 91 \end{array} \quad \begin{array}{r} 22 \\ +38 \\ \hline \textcircled{66} \end{array} \quad \begin{array}{r} 39 \\ +26 \\ \hline 65 \end{array} \quad \begin{array}{r} 43 \\ +28 \\ \hline \textcircled{72} \end{array} \quad \begin{array}{r} 19 \\ +68 \\ \hline 87 \end{array}$$

Page 82

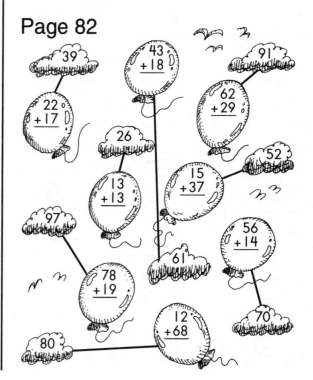

291

ANSWERS

Page 83

$4 + 5 + 6 = \underline{15}$ $6 + 7 + 5 = \underline{18}$

$2 + 3 + 7 = \underline{12}$ $9 + 2 + 1 = \underline{12}$

$5 + 1 + 2 = \underline{8}$ $3 + 3 + 3 = \underline{9}$

$8 + 1 + 3 = \underline{12}$ $4 + 2 + 1 = \underline{7}$

Page 84

Rabbit wins.

Page 85

$3 - 1 = \underline{2}$ $3 - 2 = \underline{1}$

$8 - 5 = \underline{3}$ $7 - 4 = \underline{3}$

$6 - 3 = \underline{3}$ $10 - 2 = \underline{8}$

$$\begin{array}{r} 4 \\ -3 \\ \hline 1 \end{array} \qquad \begin{array}{r} 9 \\ -5 \\ \hline 4 \end{array} \qquad \begin{array}{r} 7 \\ -2 \\ \hline 5 \end{array} \qquad \begin{array}{r} 6 \\ -1 \\ \hline 5 \end{array}$$

$$\begin{array}{r} 8 \\ -4 \\ \hline 4 \end{array} \qquad \begin{array}{r} 8 \\ -2 \\ \hline 6 \end{array} \qquad \begin{array}{r} 9 \\ -8 \\ \hline 1 \end{array} \qquad \begin{array}{r} 9 \\ -9 \\ \hline 0 \end{array}$$

Page 86

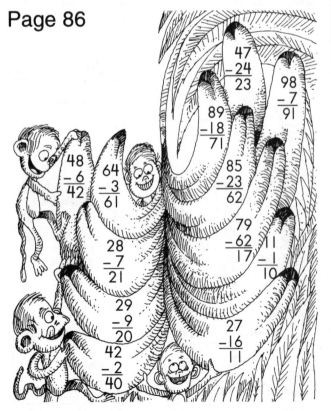

Page 87

7, 9, 16	5, 3, 8	6, 5, 11
$7 + 9 = \underline{16}$	$5 + \underline{3} = 8$	$\underline{6} + \underline{5} = \underline{11}$
$9 + 7 = \underline{16}$	$3 + \underline{5} = 8$	$\underline{5} + 6 = \underline{11}$
$16 - 9 = \underline{7}$	$8 - 5 = \underline{3}$	$\underline{11} - 6 = \underline{5}$
$16 - 7 = \underline{9}$	$8 - 3 = 5$	$\underline{11} - 5 = \underline{6}$

7, 8, 15	5, 14, 19	9, 3, 12
$\underline{7} + \underline{8} = \underline{15}$	$\underline{5} + \underline{14} = \underline{19}$	$\underline{9} + \underline{3} = \underline{12}$
$\underline{8} + \underline{7} = \underline{15}$	$\underline{14} + \underline{5} = \underline{19}$	$\underline{3} + \underline{9} = \underline{12}$
$\underline{15} - \underline{7} = \underline{8}$	$\underline{19} - \underline{14} = \underline{5}$	$\underline{12} - \underline{3} = \underline{9}$
$\underline{15} - \underline{8} = \underline{7}$	$\underline{19} - \underline{5} = \underline{14}$	$\underline{12} - \underline{9} = \underline{3}$

Page 88

6, 8, 14	3, 18, 21	6, 13, 19
$\underline{6} + \underline{8} = \underline{14}$	$\underline{3} + \underline{18} = \underline{21}$	$\underline{6} + \underline{13} = \underline{19}$
$\underline{8} + \underline{6} = \underline{14}$	$\underline{18} + \underline{3} = \underline{21}$	$\underline{13} + \underline{6} = \underline{19}$
$\underline{14} - \underline{8} = \underline{6}$	$\underline{21} - \underline{18} = \underline{3}$	$\underline{19} - \underline{13} = \underline{6}$
$\underline{14} - \underline{6} = \underline{8}$	$\underline{21} - \underline{3} = \underline{18}$	$\underline{19} - \underline{6} = \underline{13}$

4, 16, 20	3, 15, 18	5, 17, 22
$\underline{4} + \underline{16} = \underline{20}$	$\underline{3} + \underline{15} = \underline{18}$	$\underline{5} + \underline{17} = \underline{22}$
$\underline{16} + \underline{4} = \underline{20}$	$\underline{15} + \underline{3} = \underline{18}$	$\underline{17} + \underline{5} = \underline{22}$
$\underline{20} - \underline{16} = \underline{4}$	$\underline{18} - \underline{15} = \underline{3}$	$\underline{22} - \underline{17} = \underline{5}$
$\underline{20} - \underline{4} = \underline{16}$	$\underline{18} - \underline{3} = \underline{15}$	$\underline{22} - \underline{5} = \underline{17}$

Page 89

ANSWERS

Page 90

The sea lion had the most mistakes.

Page 91

Page 92

$$\overset{6\ 14}{\cancel{7}\cancel{4}} \\ -37 \\ \hline 37$$

$$\overset{4\ 10}{\cancel{5}\cancel{0}} \\ -25 \\ \hline 25$$

$$\overset{7\ 16}{\cancel{8}\cancel{6}} \\ -17 \\ \hline 69$$

$$\overset{3\ 12}{\cancel{4}\cancel{2}} \\ -13 \\ \hline 29$$

$$\overset{2\ 11}{\cancel{3}\cancel{1}} \\ -\ 9 \\ \hline 22$$

$$\overset{5\ 15}{\cancel{6}\cancel{5}} \\ -27 \\ \hline 38$$

$$\overset{8\ 12}{\cancel{9}\cancel{2}} \\ -33 \\ \hline 59$$

$$\overset{6\ 11}{\cancel{7}\cancel{1}} \\ -18 \\ \hline 53$$

$$\overset{5\ 12}{\cancel{6}\cancel{2}} \\ -24 \\ \hline 38$$

$$\overset{7\ 14}{\cancel{8}\cancel{4}} \\ -46 \\ \hline 38$$

Page 93

$$4 \\ +2 \\ \hline 6$$

$$8 \\ +6 \\ \hline 14$$

$$29 \\ +7 \\ \hline 36$$

$$\overset{5\ 13}{\cancel{6}\cancel{3}} \\ -24 \\ \hline 39$$

$$14 \\ -6 \\ \hline 8$$

$$8 \\ +3 \\ \hline 11$$

$$5 \\ +2 \\ \hline 7$$

$$11 \\ +7 \\ \hline 18$$

$$11 \\ -3 \\ \hline 8$$

$$55 \\ +5 \\ \hline 60$$

$$12 \\ +1 \\ \hline 13$$

$$14 \\ -13 \\ \hline 1$$

$$5 \\ +7 \\ \hline 12$$

$$66 \\ +34 \\ \hline 100$$

$$9 \\ -3 \\ \hline 6$$

Page 94

$$145 \\ +23 \\ \hline 168$$

$$251 \\ +48 \\ \hline 299$$

$$305 \\ +123 \\ \hline 428$$

$$500 \\ +232 \\ \hline 732$$

$$823 \\ +165 \\ \hline 988$$

$$750 \\ -300 \\ \hline 450$$

$$387 \\ -15 \\ \hline 372$$

$$923 \\ -322 \\ \hline 601$$

$$398 \\ -266 \\ \hline 132$$

$$434 \\ -22 \\ \hline 412$$

Page 95

You'll get 9 if you add 5 to me. Just what number can I be? What number am I? __4__	Take 3 away, then take 3 more, And you'll have 3 to keep in store. What number am I? __9__
Take 4 away from me, now add 3, Then add 2 more and 9 you'll see! What number am I? __8__	Add 5 to me and now add 3, Now take away 1, and 8 I'll be! What number am I? __1__
Take 7 away from me, now add 4, And you get 7—no less, no more! What number am I? __10__	Add 6 to me, then take away 5, You'll have 15, and that's no jive! What number am I? __14__

ANSWERS

Page 96

Read each question. Look at the picture. Write your answers.

How many sneakers are on the floor? __6__

Draw 2 more sneakers. Now how many are there? __8__

How many umbrellas do you see? __6__

Cross out 2 umbrellas. Now how many are there? __4__

How many boots do you see? __4__

Draw 4 boots. Now how many are there? __8__

How many socks do you see? __10__

Cross out 4 socks. Now how many? __6__

Page 97

The balloon man had 8 balloons. He sold 2.
3 floated away. Now how many does he have? __3__

Did you add or subtract? __subtract__

The hot dog vendor sold 3 hot dogs.
Then 2 children came and each bought one. How many did he sell? __5__

Did you add or subtract? __add__

How many triangle flags do you see? __6__
Draw 4 flags. Now how many are there? __10__

Did you add or subtract? __add__

There are 6 people on the ferris wheel.
There are 5 people on the merry-go-round.

How many people in all on rides? __11__

Did you add or subtract? __add__

Page 98

Read each story. Write the **equation**.

1. There are **215** kids in Bill's school. [215]

   There are **110** boys in the school. [110]

   How many girls go to Bill's school? [105]

2. The cafeteria served **189** hot lunches on Monday. [189]

   They served **176** lunches on Friday. [176]

   How many fewer people ate lunch on Friday? [13]

3. Our basketball team scored **42** points in the first half. [67]

   The other team scored **67**. [42]

   How many points do we need to catch up? [25]

Page 99

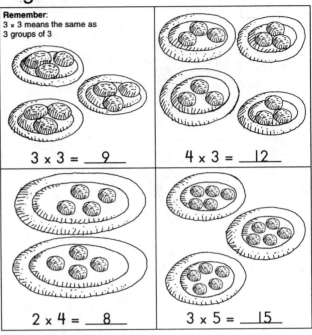

Remember:
3 x 3 means the same as
3 groups of 3

$3 \times 3 = 9$

$4 \times 3 = 12$

$2 \times 4 = 8$

$3 \times 5 = 15$

Page 100

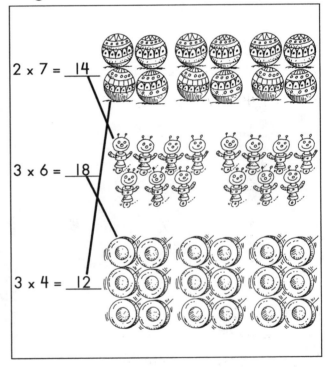

$2 \times 7 = 14$

$3 \times 6 = 18$

$3 \times 4 = 12$

Page 101

$5 \times 4 = 20$

$2 \times 7 = 14$

$3 \times 2 = 6$

ANSWERS

Page 102

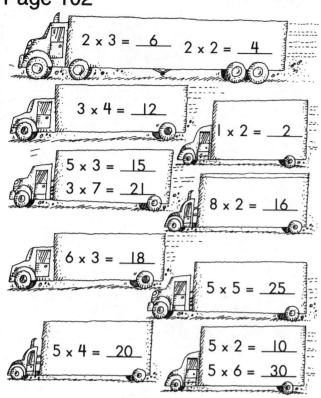

$2 \times 3 = \underline{6}$ $2 \times 2 = \underline{4}$

$3 \times 4 = \underline{12}$

$1 \times 2 = \underline{2}$

$5 \times 3 = \underline{15}$
$3 \times 7 = \underline{21}$

$8 \times 2 = \underline{16}$

$6 \times 3 = \underline{18}$

$5 \times 5 = \underline{25}$

$5 \times 4 = \underline{20}$

$5 \times 2 = \underline{10}$
$5 \times 6 = \underline{30}$

Page 103

$2 \times 4 = \underline{8}$ $5 \times 2 = \underline{10}$ $6 \times 2 = \underline{12}$

$4 \times 10 = \underline{40}$ $7 \times 5 = \underline{35}$ $10 \times 3 = \underline{30}$

$2 \times 7 = \underline{14}$ $6 \times 5 = \underline{30}$ $4 \times 3 = \underline{12}$

$$\begin{array}{r} 10 \\ \times 2 \\ \hline 20 \end{array} \qquad \begin{array}{r} 5 \\ \times 1 \\ \hline 5 \end{array} \qquad \begin{array}{r} 2 \\ \times 9 \\ \hline 18 \end{array}$$

$$\begin{array}{r} 6 \\ \times 3 \\ \hline 18 \end{array} \qquad \begin{array}{r} 9 \\ \times 3 \\ \hline 27 \end{array} \qquad \begin{array}{r} 8 \\ \times 2 \\ \hline 16 \end{array}$$

Page 104

Gasoline

$1.20 a <u>gallon</u>

To Chicago

110 <u>miles</u>

- temperature by <u>degrees</u>.

- weight by pounds and <u>ounces</u>.

- height by feet and <u>inches</u>.

- milk by pints and <u>quarts</u>.

- spices by the <u>teaspoon</u>.

Page 105

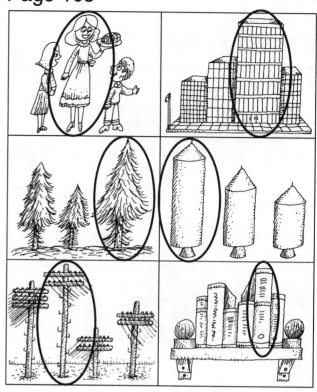

Page 106

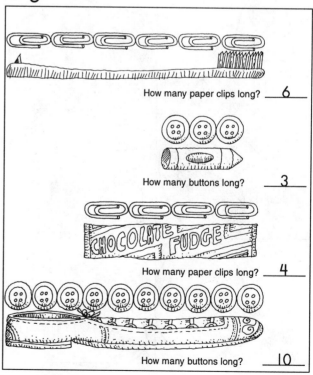

How many paper clips long? __6__

How many buttons long? __3__

How many paper clips long? __4__

How many buttons long? __10__

295

ANSWERS

Page 107

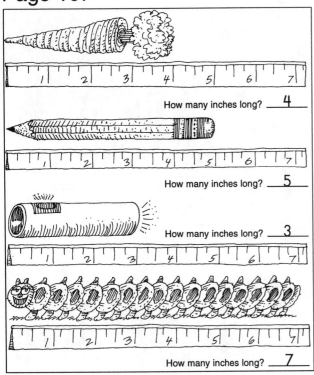

How many inches long? __4__

How many inches long? __5__

How many inches long? __3__

How many inches long? __7__

Page 108

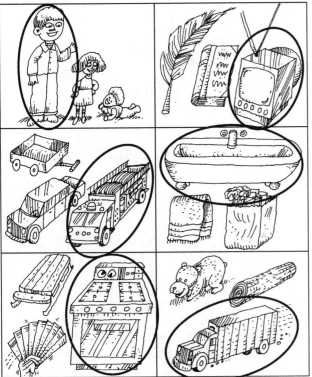

Page 109

Page 110

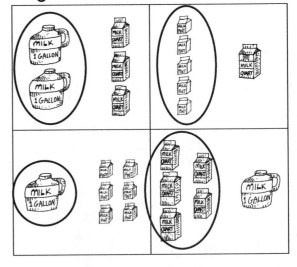

Page 111

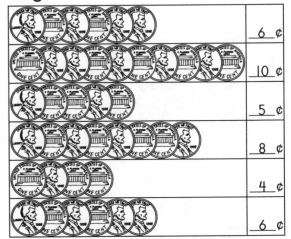

6 ¢

10 ¢

5 ¢

8 ¢

4 ¢

6 ¢

ANSWERS

Page 112

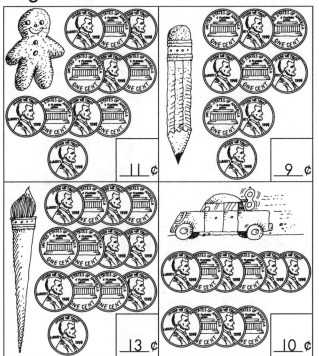

11 ¢

9 ¢

13 ¢

10 ¢

Page 113

	4	20 ¢
	7	35 ¢
	5	25 ¢
	8	40 ¢
	3	15 ¢
	6	30 ¢

Page 114

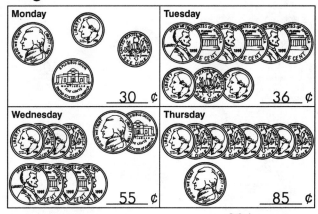

Monday	Tuesday
30 ¢	36 ¢
Wednesday	**Thursday**
55 ¢	85 ¢

Now add the sums. How much did Jan collect in all? 206¢

Page 115

How many quarters can you find in the picture below? 2

How many dimes? 5   How many nickels? 7

How many pennies? 10   How many coins in all? 24

Page 116

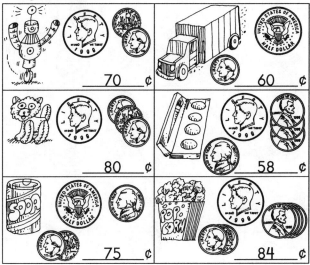

70 ¢

60 ¢

80 ¢

58 ¢

75 ¢

84 ¢

ANSWERS

Page 117

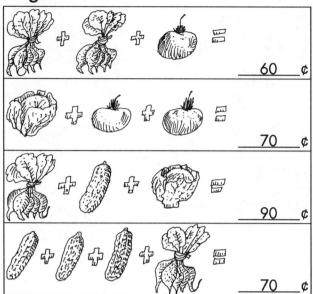

60 ¢

70 ¢

90 ¢

70 ¢

Page 118

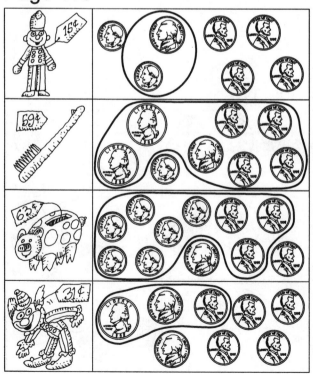

Page 119

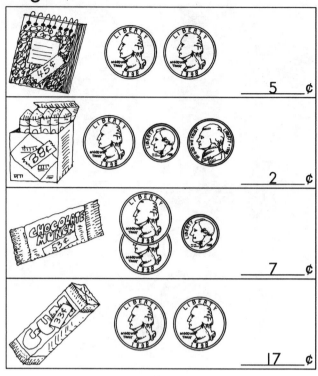

5 ¢

2 ¢

7 ¢

17 ¢

Page 120

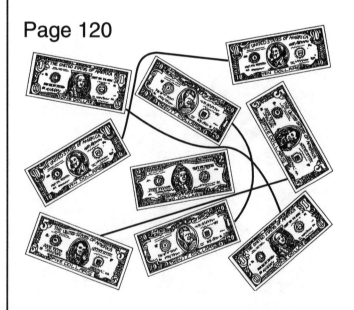

298

ANSWERS

Page 121

_____1_____ ¢

_____25_____ ¢

_____44_____ ¢

_____21_____ ¢

Page 122

Read each question. Circle each answer.

1. How many kids voted for chocolate? **(8)** 9 7
2. How many kids voted for chocolate chip? 5 **(6)** 4
3. How many kids voted for strawberry? 4 2 **(3)**
4. How many kids voted for bubblegum? **(5)** 6 7
5. Which flavor is the **most** popular with Mr. Curry's class? _chocolate_

Page 123

1. How many games has Nicole won? _____3_____
2. How many games has Alan won? _____4_____
3. Who has won the most games? _Sabrina_
4. Who has won the fewest games? _Bobby_
5. Did Nicole win more games than Eric?   Yes **(No)**
6. Did Sabrina win 2 games more than Alan? **(Yes)** No
7. Who won 3 games more than Nicole? _Sabrina_

Page 124

1. How many books did Jenny read? _____7_____
2. How many books did Paula read? _____8_____
3. Who read the most books? _Luis_
4. Who read the fewest books? _Rosita_
5. Did Jenny read more books than Rosita?   **(Yes)** No
6. Did Peter read 3 books more than Jenny? **(Yes)** No
7. Who read 3 books fewer than Luis? _Paula_

Page 125

How many squares? __6__   How many circles? __10__
How many triangles? __9__   How many rectangles? __8__

Page 127

Page 128

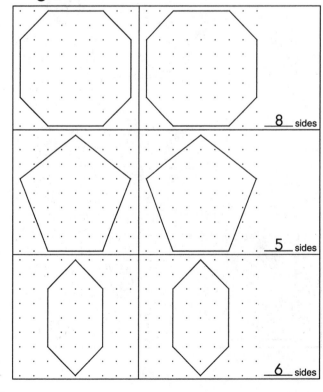

__8__ sides

__5__ sides

__6__ sides

ANSWERS

Page 129

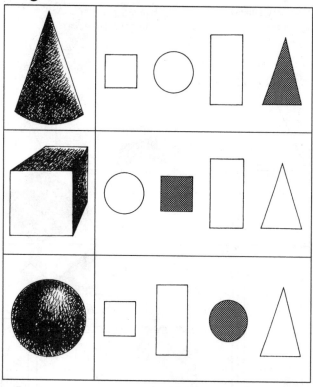

Page 130

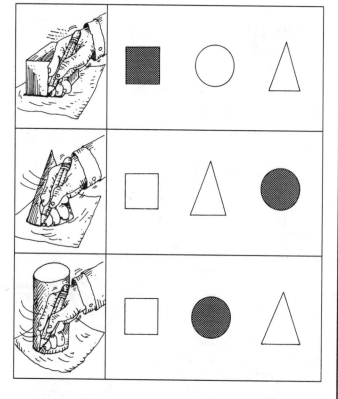

Page 131

$2 + 3 + 4 = 9$

Page 132

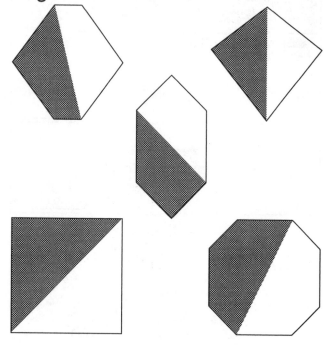

Page 133

ANSWERS

Page 134

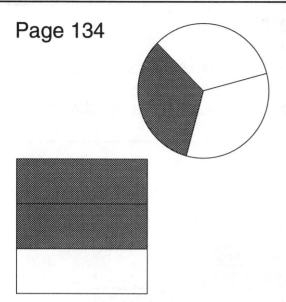

Page 135

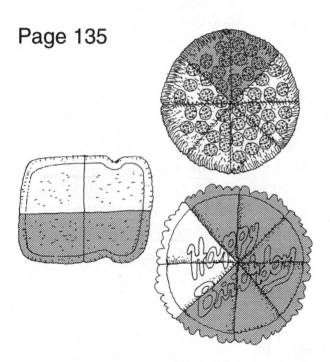

Page 138

Pandas are black and white.

The animals

Pandas eat bamboo shoots.

In the zoo

Is the bamboo yummy?

Now the pandas

Did you know pandas come from China?

Page 139

_S_ "We went to the carnival last week."

_Q_ "Did you eat cotton candy?"

_S_ "Yes, and I got a red balloon."

_S_ "I wish I had a blue balloon."

_Q_ "Did your little brother go on the merry-go-round?"

_S_ "No, he was too scared to go."

_Q_ "Was the carnival fun?"

_S_ "Yes, I wish you could have been there."

_S_ "Maybe I can go next time the carnival comes to town."

Page 140

There are many people at the party.

Are there many people at the party?

Will Rosita break the piñata?

Rosita will break the piñata.

This party is fun.

Is this party fun?

The cake will be yummy.

Will the cake be yummy?

Rosita is my best friend.

Is Rosita my best friend?

Will you come to my party next week?

You will come to my party next week.

Page 142

I'm glad we came to the beach.

Help me make a sand castle.

Here comes a big wave!

Will the wave knock down our castle?

Yes, but we can make another.

Come on, it's time to go.

Page 144

Mark and I — ride the same bus to school.

That dog — barks a lot.

The clown — juggled the balls.

Our class went to the library.

Joey found a book about space.

The librarian stamps our books.

The library is a nice place.

I'm going to go back next week.

ANSWERS

Page 145

Read each sentence. Then write the **subject** on the line.

The baby is one year old. — **The baby**

My dad drives a bus. — **My dad**

Grandma baked a pie. — **Grandma**

Our cat had kittens. — **Our cat**

Read each sentence. Then write the **predicate** on the line.

Our teacher came to my house. — **came to my house**

My family has a new car. — **has a new car**

That chair is broken. — **is broken**

Books are fun to read. — **are fun to read**

Draw lines to match the sentence parts.

Subject	Predicate
Trees	hurt my feet.
My shoes	lives underground.
A groundhog	has been very cold.
The weather	grow in a forest.

Trees → grow in a forest.
My shoes → hurt my feet.
A groundhog → lives underground.
The weather → has been very cold.

Page 146

The snow <u>covers the ground</u>.

<u>The girl</u> is making a snowman.

The children <u>throw snowballs</u>.

<u>The hill</u> is slippery and steep!

The man <u>skis</u>.

Page 147

Katie likes ladybugs. So does her sister.

<u>Katie likes ladybugs and so does her sister.</u>

My favorite class is gym. My sister likes art better.

<u>My favorite class is gym but my sister likes art better.</u>

Page 148

Max is sad. His dog is lost.

<u>Max is sad because his dog is lost.</u>

We can go to the zoo. We can play in the park.

<u>We can go to the zoo or we can play in the park.</u>

Page 149

Here comes (Chris.)
We will ride to the (park.)
We will meet our (friends) in (Cresky Park)
We ride our (bikes) every (Saturday.)
Do you have a (bike) too?

Page 150

We went to (New York City) on vacation.
Dad took me to a show at (Radio City Music Hall)
We saw my cousin (Lin Yu) in a play on (Broadway)
On (Saturday,) (Dad) and I went to the (Bronx Zoo)
On (Sunday,) we took a walk in (Central Park)
Then we flew home to (Springfield.)

Page 151

flower	flowers
hat	hats
book	books
bowl	bowls

ANSWERS

Page 152

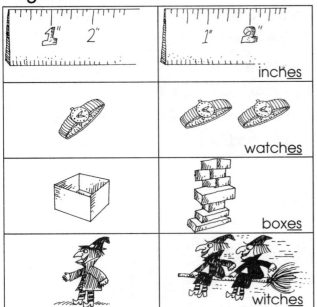

inch**es**

watch**es**

box**es**

witch**es**

Page 153

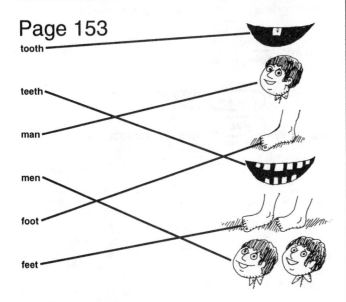

tooth

teeth

man

men

foot

feet

Page 154

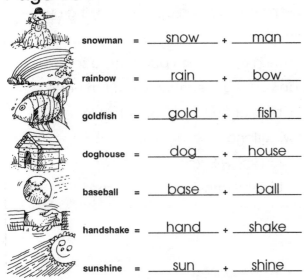

snowman	=	snow	+	man
rainbow	=	rain	+	bow
goldfish	=	gold	+	fish
doghouse	=	dog	+	house
baseball	=	base	+	ball
handshake	=	hand	+	shake
sunshine	=	sun	+	shine

Page 155

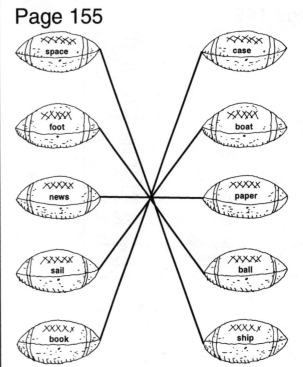

space — case
foot — boat
news — paper
sail — ball
book — ship

Page 156

Some kids (ride) a bus.
Pam's mother (drives) her to school.
We (meet) outside.
We (go) to our classroom.
At lunch time, we (eat) lunch together.

Page 157

Mother grow / **(grows)** flowers in her garden.

Rick and Mother **(work)** / works in the garden.

Rick pick / **(picks)** some pretty flowers.

We all **(eat)** / eats tomatoes for dinner!

Do you **(like)** / likes to grow things, too?

303

ANSWERS

Page 158

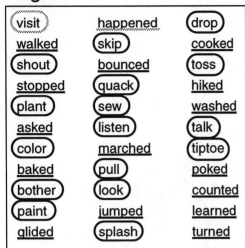

visit	happened	drop
walked	skip	cooked
shout	bounced	toss
stopped	quack	hiked
plant	sew	washed
asked	listen	talk
color	marched	tiptoe
baked	pull	poked
bother	look	counted
paint	jumped	learned
glided	splash	turned

Page 159

We (am/are) jumping rope.

I (am/is) turning the rope.

(Are/Is) he doing a flip?

I (am/was) glad you (are/is) here now.

Lots of people (is/are) watching.

Page 160

I (go/went) to another camp last year.

(Do/Did) you like it there?

No, I (like/liked) this camp better.

I (am/was) glad you are here now.

Do you (want/wanted) a hot dog?

No, I (eat/ate) a big breakfast.

Well, I (am/was) hungry now!

Please (give/gave) me a hot dog!

Page 161

I have to go to the dentist.

I hope I don't have any cavities.

The dentist has special tools to fix teeth.

Last year I had a cavity.

The dentist had to fill the hole in my tooth.

I had a bad time.

Page 162

Long ago the Pilgrims (come/came) to America.

The Pilgrims (have/had) a Thanksgiving party.

Now we (celebrate/celebrated) Thanksgiving every year.

My Mother (cook/cooks) turkey for dinner.

We always (give/gave) thanks for our food.

Page 163

"I like to eat apples."

"I had a pear, but my brother ate it."

"When you plant an apple seed, it grows into a tree."

"I once grew a bean pod from a seed."

"Can you see the mountains from here?"

"No, but I once saw a mountain in Switzerland."

"Do you know Sam?"

"No, but my father knew his father."

ANSWERS

Page 164

 <u>He</u> had a wagon. <u>She</u> had some pumpkins. <u>They</u> put the pumpkins in the wagon. <u>It</u> bumped down the street.

 Alan saw his neighbor. "Do <u>you</u> want to buy a pumpkin?" asked Alan. The neighbor did buy two pumpkins. But <u>they</u> still had a lot of pumpkins.

 So <u>they</u> took the pumpkins back home. And their mother baked some pumpkin pies. <u>She</u> is a very good cook!

Page 165

Bobby, Eric, and <u>I</u> (me) like to hike.

Mom made snacks for my friends and <u>I</u> (me) to take along.

"<u>I</u> (me) want to go, too," said my little sister.

"She's not coming, is she?" Bobby asked <u>I</u> (me)

"No," <u>I</u> (me) said. "She's too little."

<u>I</u> (me) looked at my sister.

"Later you can play a game with my friends and <u>I</u> (me)," <u>I</u> (me) told her.

She smiled, then <u>I</u> (me) waved good-bye.

My friends and <u>I</u> (me) went hiking!

Page 166

Kathy has a cat.

It is <u>Kathy's</u> cat.

Joe has a bike.

It is <u>Joe's</u> bike.

Mom has two hats.

They are <u>Mom's</u> hats.

Page 167

Those are (belonging to Sam) gloves. __Sam's__

Are these (belonging to some girls) coats? __girls'__

Who left this (belonging to a boy) hat? __boy's__

What is that in (belonging to Dad) hand? __Dad's__

I think it's (belonging to Jana) coat. __Jana's__

Are we going home in your (belonging to mom) car? __mom's__

Page 168

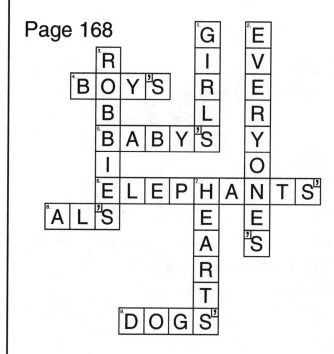

Page 169

<u>We</u> (Our) school had a carnival. Lots of kids came with <u>they</u> (their) parents.

"Are you going to get <u>you</u> (your) face painted?" asked <u>mine</u> (my) friend Courtney.

"Yes," I said, "I want it just like <u>your</u> (yours)!"

Dad bought a plant for <u>him</u> (his) office. Mom sold lots of <u>she</u> (her) cookies.

Courtney and I bought some of <u>her</u> (hers) when we got hungry. <u>Our</u> (We) made

lots of money to help the school.

Page 170

There is <u>a</u> banana on the table.

I think I'll have <u>an</u> apple.

Roger drank <u>a</u> glass of milk.

Is there <u>an</u> orange in the basket?

No, but I have <u>a</u> can of orange soda.

ANSWERS

Page 171

Helen has a (yellow) boat.
It has (big) (white) sails.
My boat has (striped) sails.
It is a (nice) (warm) day.
I see lots of (fluffy) clouds.
Later I'll fly my (new) kite.
It is (green).

Page 172

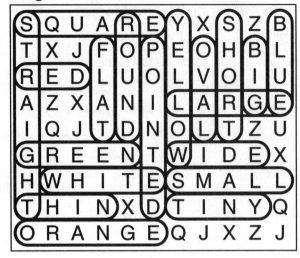

(funny)	come	(soft)	(sandy)	(sweet)
(red)	(hard)	cloud	book	candy
(sad)	(warm)	(cold)	(green)	pencil
bear	(happy)	coat	(loud)	tree
(pink)	fish	(tall)	(furry)	(angry)

Write an **adjective** from the box to complete each sentence.
Underline the **noun** or **pronoun** it describes.

My puppy has a furry coat.

Please turn down that loud music!

A giraffe is very tall.

I like to play on a sandy beach.

I stepped on a hard rock!

Look at the funny clown!

That bear does not look happy.

Ice is cold.

Sunshine makes me feel warm.

The tree is green.

Page 173

We saw (some) dolphins.
(Every) dolphin did tricks.
The trainer rode on (one) dolphin.
Then (two) dolphins leaped in the air.
The (three) dolphins even played basketball!
The dolphins had (some) fish as a reward.
There were (50) people at the show.
(Many) people stayed for the next show.

Page 174

S	Q	U	A	R	E	Y	X	S	Z	B
T	X	J	F	O	P	E	O	H	B	L
R	E	D	L	U	O	L	V	O	I	U
A	Z	X	A	N	I	L	A	R	G	E
I	Q	J	T	D	N	O	L	T	Z	U
G	R	E	E	N	T	W	I	D	E	X
H	W	H	I	T	E	S	M	A	L	L
T	H	I	N	X	D	T	I	N	Y	Q
O	R	A	N	G	E	Q	J	X	Z	J

Page 175

Gwen is taller than her sister.

Matt is the tallest kid in our class.

I am younger than Pam.

But I'm older than Matt.

Recess today was shorter than yesterday,
    because it's colder today than yesterday!

Last Friday was the coldest day all year.

And the snow was deeper than before.

I made the oddest snowman you'll ever see.

Slow down, you're walking faster than I am!

Page 176

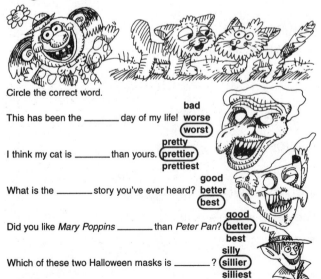

Circle the correct word.

This has been the _____ day of my life!
bad
worse
(worst)

I think my cat is _____ than yours.
pretty
(prettier)
prettiest

What is the _____ story you've ever heard?
good
better
(best)

Did you like *Mary Poppins* _____ than *Peter Pan*?
good
(better)
best

Which of these two Halloween masks is _____?
silly
(sillier)
silliest

306

ANSWERS

Page 177

I won a prize (yesterday.) __when__

I ran (speedily) in the race. __how__

I (never) thought I would win. __when__

I marched (proudly) with other winners. __how__

I stood (up) on a stage. __where__

I looked (around.) __where__

My friends smiled (happily) at me. __how__

Page 178

I tried to paint <u>neatly</u>.

But someone outside yelled <u>loudly</u>.

I <u>carelessly</u> splashed the paint!

My friend Jan <u>quickly</u> cleaned it up.

Jan had <u>cleverly</u> hidden a mouse in her picture.

I looked <u>closely</u>, but I couldn't find it.

We painted <u>happily</u> all afternoon.

Page 179

Does a snail move _____ than a turtle?
slowly
(more slowly)
most slowly

Maybe the snail is moving _____ than an ant.
quickly
(more quickly)
most quickly

But which of the three animals can move _____ ?
quickly
more quickly
(most quickly)

The rabbit thought the turtle went _____ .
(slowly)
more slowly
most slowly

But the turtle raced _____ than the rabbit!
cleverly
(more cleverly)
most cleverly

Page 180

The cat in the hat __The Cat in the Hat__

The little princess __The Little Princess__

bread and jam for Frances __Bread and Jam for Frances__

snow white and rose red __Snow White and Rose Red__

Page 181

I + (a)m = I'm

We + (wi)ll = we'll

They + (ha)ve = they've

You + (a)re = you're

Page 182

What letter does the apostrophe replace in **I am**? __a__

What letter does the apostrophe replace in **is not**? __o__

What letters does the apostrophe replace in **can not**? __no__

What letter does the apostrophe replace in **she is**? __i__

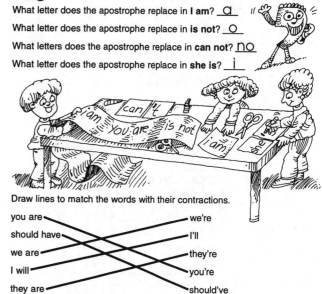

Draw lines to match the words with their contractions.

you are — you're
should have — should've
we are — we're
I will — I'll
they are — they're

Page 183

It <u>isn't</u> time for the game yet.

Mary <u>doesn't</u> care who wins, but I do.

The teams <u>haven't</u> taken the field.

Jack likes the Tigers, but they <u>aren't</u> very good.

If we <u>don't</u> score soon, we <u>won't</u> win.

ANSWERS

Page 184

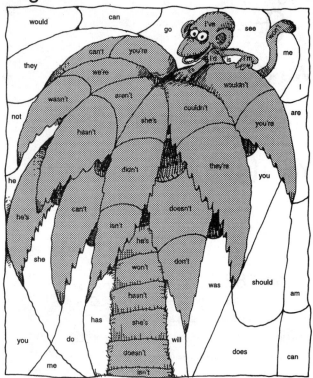

Page 188

Page 186

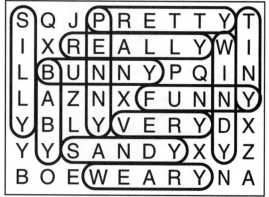

Page 189

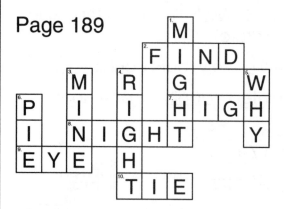

Page 187

The (train) (came) to the (station.)
I hope it wasn't (late.)
Is it going to (rain) (today?)
If it does, the (mail) will be (late.)
(Stay) right here.
Don't (wait) for me in Watertown.
(Amy) wants to (paint) on the (train!)

Page 190

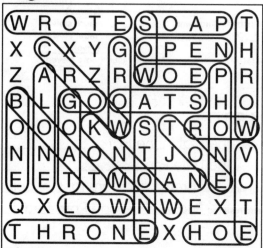

ANSWERS

Page 191

nomo	moon
leub	blue
dofo	food
leuc	clue
moor	room
ture	true
snopo	spoon
lonbloa	balloon
onon	noon

Page 192

The ice is thick, so let's go <u>skating</u>.

Shh! The baby's <u>sleeping</u>.

You make me happy, so I'm <u>smiling</u>.

The sun is <u>hiding</u> behind the clouds.

I can use my new sled because it's <u>snowing</u>!

I'm <u>reading</u> the most exciting book.

Have you been <u>thinking</u> it over?

You should be <u>going</u> to bed!

He's been <u>playing</u> baseball for years.

Page 193

Crossword:
- B A T T I N G
- S K I P P I N G
- H U G G E D
- R U B B E D
- H O P P I N G
- S L E D D I N G
- D R O P P E D

Page 229

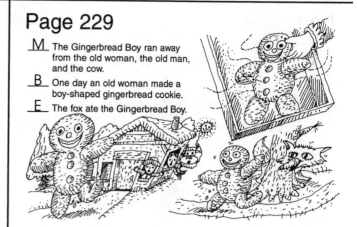

__M__ The Gingerbread Boy ran away from the old woman, the old man, and the cow.

__B__ One day an old woman made a boy-shaped gingerbread cookie.

__E__ The fox ate the Gingerbread Boy.

Page 231

"I went back to Grandpa's farm. I used to live there. Grandpa has cows and horses. The farm is nice."

"I could taste the dust as I walked up the long farm road. Then I saw the old red barn. I heard the cows mooing. I smelled hot apple pie. Then I saw Grandpa running to me. It was good to be home!"

Page 235

The name of this book is: <u>Giant Basic Skills 2nd Grade Workbook</u>

This book is written by (educational consultant): <u>Shirley Granahan</u>

The book is about: <u>Basic Skills</u>

Page 238

DEARIGN	READING
THAM	MATH
DIOATDIN	ADDITION
ARCOTFINS	FRACTIONS
PINGSELL	SPELLING
GRINWIT	WRITING
LUTYMLIP	MULTIPLY
COSPNIH	PHONICS
TENNESSEC	SENTENCES

ANSWERS

Page 239

+ D = CANDY

- C + L = OWL

C U = I SEE YOU

- BL + F + = ELEPHANT

H + ? M + ♥

Page 240

♥ *   ♥ ♦   * ▲ ▲ (▼)   * ♥ ● ★ ■

 I T   I S   T O O (2)   T I R E D !

Page 241

I have lots of teeth but I don't bite. However, I do nibble at the tangles you get in your hair! What am I?	I hang with a bunch in the warm sun. I'm yellow, good to eat, and have lots of a-PEEL! What am I?
I have a head but can't talk. I have feet but can't walk. You make me up, but I'm real. At night you lie down on me. What am I?	Look for me where people eat. I'm metal or plastic. I'm no help when you eat cereal, but I am when you eat spaghetti! What am I?

Page 242

What days will the fair be held? <u>Thursday and Friday</u>

What time is the fair? <u>4:00 to 8:00 P.M.</u>

What can people do at the fair? <u>play games, see movies, eat</u>

What will the school do with the money they make? <u>buy computers</u>

Page 243

Everyone in my class came to my party. Jennifer is in my class. Did Jennifer come to my party?

(Yes)   No   You Can't Tell

Marcie must be home by 8:00 p.m. on school nights. Monday she wants to go to a movie, but it ends at 9:30 p.m. Will Marcie go to the movie?

Yes   **(No)**   You Can't Tell

My friend Jodi moved to Springfield. There's a Springfield in Massachusetts. Did Jodi move to Massachusetts?

Yes   No   **(You Can't Tell)**

A person can get a driver's license after age 16. Ralph is 14 years old. Can he legally drive a car?

Yes   **(No)**   You Can't Tell

The train from New York had 100 people on board. The train made two stops, but none of the 100 people got off. Are there still 100 on the train?

Yes   No   **(You Can't Tell)**

Page 244

```
      J A M E S   S
    L E D A   A
  B U D D Y   M
  L     Y   A M Y
  U         Y
```

Page 245

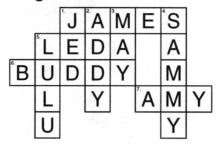

sneaker : foot = hat :

bear : cub = horse :

wing : airplane = sail :

ears : stereo = eyes :

skyscraper : buildings = pine :

rug : floor = curtain :

water : swim = snow :

ANSWERS

Page 246

Page 248

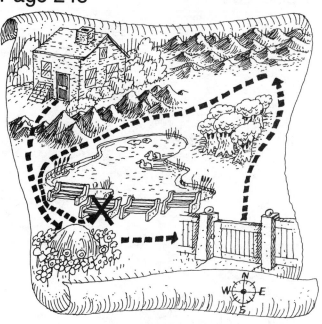

Page 247

mouse : squeak = duck : quack
age **(sound)** color

bowl : fish = hive : bees
shape **(home)** amount

ore : store = one : stone
(letters) rocks height

skin : human = feathers : bird
shape weight **(covering)**

flour : bread = milk : pudding
weight color **(ingredients)**

Now write the end to each of these analogies.

art : museum = books : ___library___

soft : loud = whisper : ___shout___

dress : silk = table : ___wood___

horn : toot = drum : ___bang___

tulip : plant = orange : ___fruit___

Page 249

carpenter
actor
teacher
writer
___doctor___
| careers |

washer
computer
bulldozer
car
___dryer___
| machines |

Mexico
England
Italy
Japan
___U.S.A___
| countries |

boom
bang
crash
POW!
___honk___
| sounds |

tree
rose
bush
grass
___vine___
| plants |

Green Eggs and Ham
Curious George
Winnie the Pooh
The Tale of
    Peter Rabbit
___Puss in Boots___
| books |

lion
koala
snake
yak
___sheep___
| animals |

ANSWERS

Page 250

Page 252

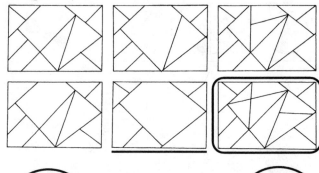

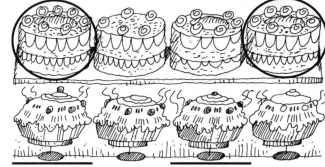

Page 251

Feature	Ball	Orange
Round	X	X
Comes in many colors	X	
Squeeze juice from it		X
Bounces	X	
Rolls	X	X
Good to eat		X
Stays usable for years	X	
Sweet to eat		X
Made of rubber	X	
Can use half of it at a time		X

Page 253

Cow	Sheep	Chicken
says "moo"	says "baa"	says "cluck"
furry	soft, wooly	feathery
lives on farms	lives on farms	lives on farms
gives milk	gives wool	lays eggs
has four legs	has four legs	has two legs
baby called calf	baby called lamb	baby called chick

ANSWERS

Page 254

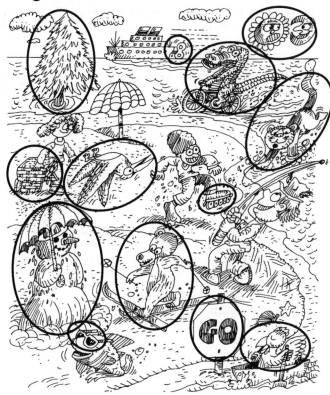

Page 255

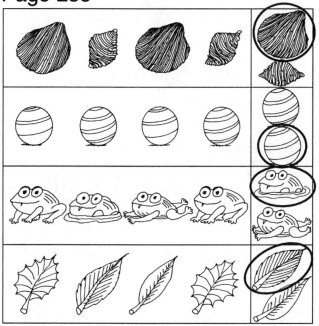

Page 256

Page 257

_6_ Cut the sandwich in half.

_3_ Spread peanut butter on one slice.

_5_ Put the two slices of bread together.

_1_ Get two slices of bread, a knife, and jars of peanut butter and jelly.

_4_ Spread jelly on the other slice.

_7_ Clean up and put things away.

_2_ Put bread on a plate.

Page 258

_2_ Pick teams.

_1_ Get a kickball.

_4_ Play kickball game.

_3_ Choose who goes first.

ANSWERS

Page 259

The first flow chart tells you how to drink milk.

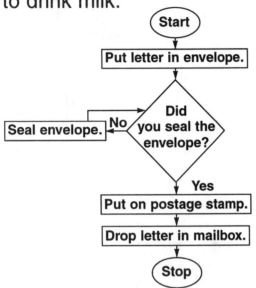

Start
→ Put letter in envelope.
→ Did you seal the envelope?
— No → Seal envelope. (loops back)
— Yes → Put on postage stamp.
→ Drop letter in mailbox.
→ Stop

Page 261

1. Grandpa	83 years		1. Ralph	142 pounds
2. Dad	43		2. Dan	121
3. Mom	37		3. Ken	97
4. Jasper	7		4. Ruth	86
5. Melissa	1		5. Tessa	51

Ranked by: height / **age** / weight

Ranked by: height / age / **weight**

1. Eat an apple		1. 6:00 a.m.
2. Frost a cake		2. 10:00 a.m.
3. Read a recipe		3. Noon
4. Bake a pie		4. 6:00 p.m.
5. Write a cookbook		5. 11:00 p.m.

Ranked from: **Easy to difficult** / Young to old / Thin to fat

Ranked from: Fast to slow / Old to young / **Early to late**

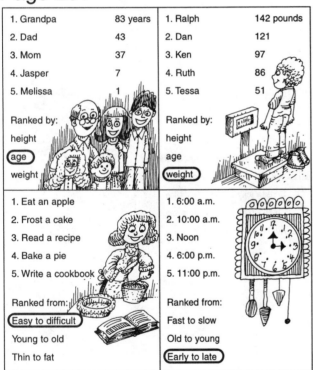

Page 262

IF YOU LIKE THIS KIND OF PUZZLE, MAKE ONE FOR YOURSELF

Page 263

If yesterday was Monday, **then** tomorrow will be Wednesday.
(**True**)   Not certain

If it doesn't rain today, **then** it will rain tomorrow.
True   (**Not certain**)

If I like chocolate ice cream, **then** my mother likes it too.
True   (**Not certain**)

If the ice cream shop is closed, **then** you can't buy ice cream there.
(**True**)   Not certain

If the teacher gives a test, **then** everyone will past it.
True   (**Not certain**)

Page 264

"**If** it's nice on Tuesday **and** I can get off work, **then** I'll be at the game," Bill said. Bill had to work Tuesday. Did he go to the game?
Yes   (**No**)

"**If** you were absent yesterday **or** missed the spelling test last week, **then** please raise your hand," said the teacher. You've been in school all week. You took the test last week. Should you raise your hand?
Yes   (**No**)

If your birthday was on December 31 this year **and** you were 7 years old, **then** next year on December 31 you'll be 8 years old.
(**Yes**)   No

Page 265

Color the diamond-shaped kites red.
How many are there? __5__

Color the box kites blue.
How many are there? __3__

Color the dragon kites green.
How many are there? __2__

Color the fish kites yellow.
How many are there? __4__

Page 266

B	O	E	C	A	L	K	C	E	N	Q
S	B	D	B	N	G	I	K	M	O	Z
A	S	H	O	E	S	H	E	O	F	L
N	A	B	O	C	A	R	F	A	R	F
D	N	X	T	K	Y	L	E	N	A	M
F	D	A	S	T	C	M	I	T	C	K
O	A	G	M	I	T	T	E	N	S	I
O	L	C	S	E	G	L	O	V	X	M
T	S	S	E	V	O	L	G	Q	A	E

ANSWERS

Page 268

Page 271

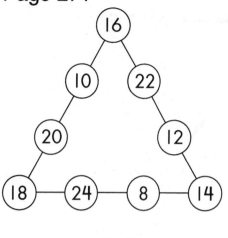

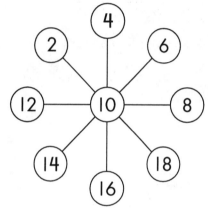

Page 269

	Cake	Cookie	Muffin	Pie
Alex	O	✓	O	O
Claire	O	O	O	✓
Jenny	O	O	✓	O
Patrick	✓	O	O	O

Page 270

	Cat	Dog	Hamster	Lizard
Andy	O	✓	O	O
Erin	O	O	O	✓
Maggie	✓	O	O	O
Stuart	O	O	✓	O

Page 272

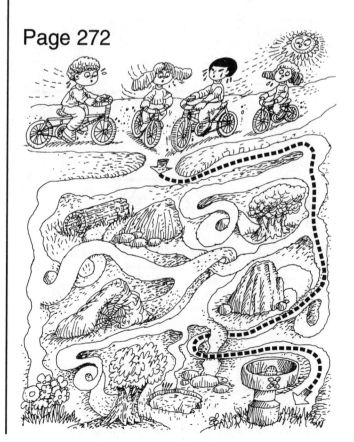

ANSWERS

Page 273

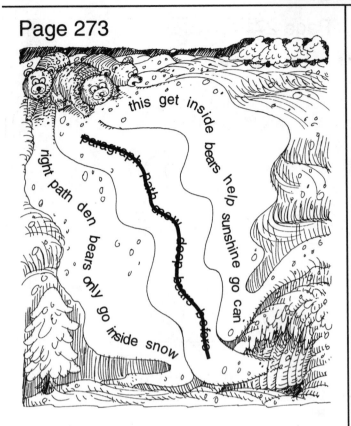

Page 274

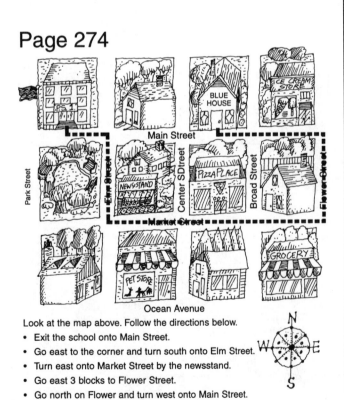

Look at the map above. Follow the directions below.

- Exit the school onto Main Street.
- Go east to the corner and turn south onto Elm Street.
- Turn east onto Market Street by the newsstand.
- Go east 3 blocks to Flower Street.
- Go north on Flower and turn west onto Main Street.
- Go past the ice cream shop and stop in front of the blue house.
- Look across Main Street.
  What building do you see? **Pizza Place**

Page 275

N O W   Y O U   H A V E   A L L
T H E   S K I L L S   Y O U   N E E D!

Page 276

What did the bunny say when he saw his tail?

What letter is in THERE but not in HERE?   T
What letter is in HAIR but not in AIR?   H
What letter is in RIDE but not in DARE?   I
What letter is in SEVEN but not in EVEN?   S

What letter is in MOTHER but not in OTHER?   M
What letter is in TRUCK but not in TRACK?   U
What letter is in SEW but not in WE?   S
What letter is in TON but not in NOODLE?   T

What letter is in BLUE but not in GLUE?   B
What letter is in RIDE but not in RIDING?   E

What letter is in POT but not in OPEN?   T
What letter is in SHELL but not in LESS?   H
What letter is in ONE but not in NOT?   E

What letter is in READ but not in ROAD?   E
What letter is in FINE but not in FIVE?   N
What letter is in SHADE but not in ASHES?   D

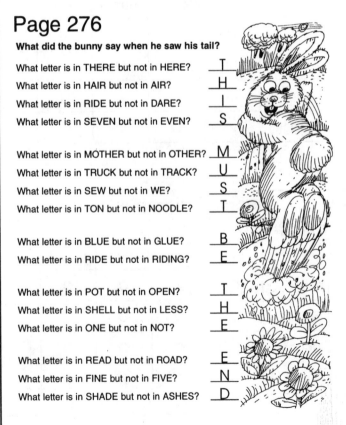

ACHIEVEMENT CHECKLIST

Use the checklist below after each session with this book. If your child had trouble with a page, find the problem skill and list the page number in the middle column. You'll want to return to it later. If your child successfully completed the pages containing a skill, put a check mark in the "Mastered" column. Your child can watch with pride as the column fills up with skills he or she has mastered.

BASIC SKILLS	Needs Work	Mastered!
ABC ORDER		
Sequencing in ABC order		
Alphabetizing words		
Recognizing letters		
PHONICS		
Short vowel sounds		
Long vowel sounds		
Double-vowel sounds		
Vowel digraphs		
Diphthongs		
Beginning consonants		
Medial consonants		
Final consonants		
The soft g rule		
The soft c rule		
Consonant blends		
Consonant digraphs		
READING SKILLS		
Visual discrimination		
Classification		
Understanding cause and effect		
Predicting outcomes		
Synonyms and Antonyms		

BASIC SKILLS	Needs Work	Mastered!
Homonyms		
Story order		
Story mapping		
Character webs		
Finding the main idea		
Drawing conclusions		
Environmental science		
Recalling details		
Comparing and contrasting		
MATH		
Skip counting		
Identifying odd and even numbers		
Ordinal numbers		
Writing equations		
Addition		
Subtraction		
Adding and subtracting multiple numbers		
Word problems		
Understanding multiplication		
Measuring		
Comparing height, weight, volume		
Money values		
Interpreting graphs		
Geometric shapes and solids		
Understanding fractions		
GRAMMAR		
Types of sentences		

BASIC SKILLS	Needs Work	Mastered!
Identifying sentence parts		
Nouns		
Forming plural nouns		
Verbs		
Subject-verb agreement		
Past and present tenses		
Irregular verbs		
Pronouns		
Possessive forms		
Using articles		
Adjectives and Adverbs		
Capitalization		
Contractions		
Word families		
Spelling		
WRITING		
Narrative paragraphs		
Writing a story		
Writing descriptively		
Writing poetry		
Journal entries		
Book reports		
THINKING SKILLS		
Making inferences		
Analogies		
Map reading		
Patterning		
Problem solving		
If...then logic		
Deduction		

Diploma

Awarded to

for extraordinary achievement in 2nd Grade Basic Skills

on this date,

CONGRATULATIONS!

Smart Kid